SEX
ISN'T THAT
SIMPLE

Richard Hettlinger

SEX ISN'T THAT SIMPLE: the new sexuality on campus

A Continuum Book
THE SEABURY PRESS · NEW YORK

The Seabury Press
815 Second Avenue
New York, N.Y. 10017

Second Printing

ACKNOWLEDGMENTS
See page 243, which constitutes an extension of this copyright page.

Copyright © 1974 by Richard F. Hettlinger
Design by Carol Basen
Printed in the United States of America

LIBRARY OF CONGRESS CATALOGING IN PUBLICATION DATA

Hettlinger, Richard Frederick.
  Sex isn't that simple.

  (A Continuum book)
  Bibliography: p. 221
    1. College students—United States—Sexual behavior.
I. Title. [DNLM: 1. Sex behavior. 2. Students.
HQ35.2 H591s 1974]
HQ35.2.H47   301.41'74'45   73–17876
ISBN 0–8164–9196–8
ISBN 0–8164–9197–6 (pbk.)

Contents

For Mary,
without whom
I would be much more
of a male chauvinist than I am.

SEX
ISN'T THAT
SIMPLE

CHAPTER I

Sex and Society

In 1721 a debate was held at Harvard on the question "Whether it be Fornication to lie with one's Sweetheart before Marriage." Such a discussion would draw few participants today. There are some students for whom the issue arises in the traditional form and for whom the question whether or not to sleep together is a central problem. But for the majority on campus the question is not *whether* but *when* and the decision has very little to do with marriage. Those who preserve their virginity are not likely to do so because they are impressed by religious or legal prohibitions against "fornication," but because they have nobody who is the contemporary equivalent of a "sweetheart." It is not a decision for or against the specific act of intercourse that concerns many men and women, but the problem of establishing the kind of relationship in which sex is appropriate and meaningful.

Unfortunately most colleges and universities give little help to students in understanding the dynamics and implications of sexual behavior. Many accept in practice (if not in theory) the proposal of the Group for the Advancement of Psychiatry that "sexual activity privately practiced with appropriate attention to the sensitivities of other people should not be the direct concern of the administration" (Eddy, 1966, p. 126).* Many offer courses covering everything from the early history of the zygote to the erotic practices of obscure preliterate tribes. Several distribute useful handbooks with information about birth control, abortion and venereal disease. These are certainly important because ignorance about these matters is remarkable, and I have included some basic information in the Appendix (pp. 187–219). But faculty members and administrators tend to fight shy of discussing questions of sexual behavior because they are controversial and involve personal values. The function of the college or university, it is often affirmed, is the cultivation of the mind, not debate about matters of private morality. Emergency service for the seriously disturbed may be an unfortunate necessity, but the emotional and social development of the student is not a primary concern.

I find this unsatisfactory, for inevitably the campus is where most students discover themselves as sexual persons. We teachers may regard sex as a very secondary issue, but it is frequently of more importance for students than lectures, papers or tests. The college campus, whether the faculty like it or not, plays the role of (among other things) the *bukumatula* in the Trobriand Islands of Melanesia. These are special houses owned by "some mature youth or young widower" in which groups of adolescent boys and girls live together at puberty and experiment sexually without benefit of parental supervision (Malinowski, 1927, p. 67). It's true that you could graduate from the *bukumatula* without allowing any academic concerns to interfere with your sexual life. Today's students who give priority to sexual exploration over intellectual explora-

---

* References are given at the back of the book (pp. 221–238) under the author's name and the year of publication.

tion will hardly succeed in completing the requirement set by the faculty (the contemporary equivalents of the "mature youth or young widower"). But I believe we fail partially in the task of education if we concern ourselves only with the academic and fail to give students the help they need to develop a healthy sexuality.

In a very thorough study of student interests at Berkeley and Stanford a group of psychiatrists found that for the majority the development of relations with other people was of paramount importance. Several hundred men and women, both as freshmen and as seniors, ranked their primary needs as (1) love and affection, (2) emotional well-being, (3) maintaining self-respect and (4) being accepted and liked by others. The authors commented: "The great stress that students put on love and affection may spring from a sense that the cultivation of these qualities is not given sufficient support in their education. They are more often encouraged to be solitary performing animals than social or communicating animals" (Katz, 1968, p. 65).

My hope is to contribute to the illumination and satisfaction of these needs. I make no claim to pure objectivity, for on this subject nobody—not even Kinsey or Masters and Johnson—is free of value judgments. But I hope to avoid dogmatism and to leave the reader free to form his or her own opinion. I do not believe that any external authority—parental, religious or academic—can determine for students what is appropriate sexual behavior. All anyone can do is to try to help people recognize the complexity of sexual relationships and develop an enjoyment of sexuality as a creative element in personal growth. We need to escape from the obsession with intercourse as *the* sex act (illustrated by the common identification of "having sex" and engaging in coitus). Instead of focusing our energies on the achievement (or avoidance) of intercourse we need to learn to enjoy sexuality as a wide range of experiences affecting all our relationships with people. Whether an individual finds intercourse an appropriate expression of a particular relationship or not, whether his or her fulfillment is heterosexual or homosexual, whether the goal is a traditional marriage, life in a commune or whatever—these seem to me quite secondary (though not unimportant) issues. What matters is that the student learns to act and think sexually without evasion, deceit or illusion; that he or she can distinguish the false myths (of the old *and* the counter cultures) from the truth; and above all that there is growth in the capacity for self-giving, sympathy and caring.

Sex at college will be most worthwhile, I suggest, if sexuality is an honest, informed and consistent expression of ever-deepening relationships to other people *short of marriage*. In some cases a permanent legal commitment during the college years may be wise. Some couples who marry early find it is the best decision they could have made. But I see these years as a period of development from which formal and legal obligations—not to mention parenthood —are usually best excluded. Certainly if a couple get married because it's the only way they can sleep together with a clear conscience, to escape from parental authority, because they've had intercourse and feel guilty, or because they've conceived a baby they are likely to run into serious problems. On the other hand those who avoid all sexual commitments out of fear or insecurity or an unexamined bondage to rigid parental or religious prohibitions are likely to remain stunted in their growth as human persons.

The campus is not an island; it's part of a larger community that puts some serious obstacles in the way of a mature and balanced sexuality. In the first place our society is highly ambivalent: it is neither clearly anti-sexual nor clearly pro-sexual; it suffers from a public schizophrenia. One critic has called it "sex-centric but sex rejecting" (Johnson, 1963). On the one hand sexual concern is inculcated in children from an early age. Little girls are encouraged to be "cute" and given dolls with well-formed breasts. Preteenagers wear two-piece swimsuits and participate in Junior Miss pageants. Deodorants, cosmetics and hair sprays are virtually essential equipment for teenage girls. Adolescent boys are expected to begin showing an interest in the other sex and are regarded with concern by their parents if they fail to do so.

The search for a partner in romantic love is assumed throughout the teens to be part of the preparation for eventual marriage. This does not, of course, include encouragement to give expression to courtship in heavy petting or intercourse: it is the external form and emotional trappings of sexual relationships that our society officially approves. It is the competitiveness, not the reality, of sex that is fostered. Teenagers are encouraged to demonstrate their ability to attract or gain attention, but discouraged from allowing themselves to become seriously involved. The dynamics of sexuality are ignored, so that when adolescents find themselves involved in petting or intercourse parental approval of the relationship is suddenly withdrawn. Girls are encouraged to develop their capacity for titillation and teasing to the full: they are expected to be admired and sought after; they are not expected to be touched below the navel. One student reported that her parents taught her that "sex was the worst thing possible until you got married, and after marriage it was the most beautiful thing you could do" (Lower, 1973, p. 65).

The double-faced character of our society is further illustrated by the use of sex in the media. While impressing on their children that sex is something sacred to be kept for marriage, the adult world has no hesitation in taking full advantage of erotic responses to sell everything from chutney (*Chut-Nut* is "the sexier chutney") to automobiles. We are invited to "Make Love Not Beds" on *Slumberdown,* to "Make out better at both ends" with *Big Tip Pall Mall Gold* and to let *John Kloss* dress us for bed when we're not the least bit sleepy. The smart boats this year are said to be wearing "topless power," and *Capri* is "the first sexy European car under $2,300." We learn from the ads "What to wear on Sunday when you won't be home till Monday" and "Where to shop for underthings if you're not thinking of wearing any." We are advised that "She'll find it hard when you kiss goodnight in *Harris Slacks*" and that it takes *Paul Maris* to get her out of her jeans. *Je Reviens* is the perfume that helps you say "no" so that he thinks you mean "not now," and *Vassarette* is the nightdress for girls who don't sleep alone. And so it goes.

What has been called the "erotization of the social backdrop" inevitably serves to stimulate sexual interest. The 1970 *Report of the Commission on Obscenity and Pornography,* while arguing against censorship and finding no evidence that pornographic materials lead to delinquency, noted that "exposure to erotic stimuli produces sexual arousal in substantial portions of both males and females" (p. 28). And the *Report of the Effects Panel* to the commission included this statement: "Among American college students, frequency of exposure to erotic materials is associated with relatively high rates of sociosexual experimentation (hugging, kissing, light and heavy petting, coitus) during both high school and college years, especially among males" (p. 219).

My point is not that our society should be less open about sex. It is the commercialization of sex combined with the attempt to deny its honest expression that I deplore. While our society uses sex to sell its goods in the marketplace it fails to recognize the tensions this climate produces. The fact that males, according to Kinsey (1948), attain their greatest sexual capacity in the late teens is given no practical recognition in the public mores, and Kinsey estimated that 85 percent of the adolescent male population could be convicted as sex offenders if law enforcement officers were efficient.

There are laws in several states forbidding many petting practices if the girl is under twenty-one, even if she consents. In some states genital contact outside marriage is technically punishable by prison sentences of up to ten years. Of course many of the legal proscriptions of sexual activity on the statute books are inoperative: but their existence reflects a dichotomy that is understandably confusing to those growing up in search of a coherent attitude to sexuality. And there are occasions on which they are put into effect. In 1973 the Pennsylvania House of Representatives voted 118 to 69 to *restore* the state's traditional ban on adultery and fornication. And in 1972 a correspondent in *Playboy* reported the case of a public employee in Florida who was threatened with the loss of his job because he was living with a woman to whom he was not married—on the basis of a statute providing for a penalty of up to two years in the state prison.

The contradictions of censorship represent another area of confusion. It is not the effectiveness of the legal prohibition on obscenity, but the principle that is significant. The implication is that sex is so virulent a danger that it requires special restriction lest it threaten the whole fabric of society. Almost any scene of violence or sadistic torture is assumed to be without serious deleterious effect on the young; but the sight of a female breast or of the human genitals is assumed to be immediately depraving. The

Motion Picture Association of America threatened an R rating for the movie *Lady Caroline Lamb* because in two scenes the actress Sarah Miles bared her bosom briefly. Her comment was apropos: "I am amused that someone thinks that a glimpse of my nipples could corrupt the youth of America," she said. "When I read statistics like one in every five people in America is either burgled or mugged, I wonder whether a glimpse of nipple now and then might help."

In an ad for one of my books the publisher included some very tasteful photographs of young children naked. One liberal (religious) weekly refused to accept the ad because it showed the genitals of a six-year-old boy and girl. In a broadcast version of *Jesus Christ Superstar* Mary Magdalene was made to sing "I've known so many men" instead of "I've had so many men." A TV presentation of the movie *Diary of a Mad Housewife* succeeded in editing out every mention of intercourse including a puerile reference to "a roll in the hay." The Painesville (Ohio) school board was petitioned by 200 parents for the removal of such books as *Rosemary's Baby* and *Catch 22* from the reading list for the eleventh grade as recently as 1971. In the same year a judge in Michigan banned Vonnegut's *Slaughterhouse Five* because of its "repetitious obscenity and immorality": and he was *not* speaking about the obscenity of the bombing of Dresden.

When the Commission on Obscenity and Pornography reported in 1970 in favor of a more honest acceptance of sexuality and a nation-wide program of sex education its work was immediately repudiated by President Nixon as "morally bankrupt." * But what is even more troubling is

---

* In the light of later events it is instructive to reread Mr. Nixon's statement of October 24, 1970. It finished thus: "Moreover, if an attitude of permissiveness were to be adopted regarding pornography, this would contribute to an atmosphere condoning anarchy in every other field—and

that *only six* U.S. senators voted in favor of a careful consideration of the commission's proposals. This, as one commentator remarked, "would be unbelievable if one were not aware of how very far we are from being able to be objective about sex and sexuality in its many forms" (Pomeroy, 1970). The 1973 decision of the Supreme Court, allowing local communities to determine what is acceptable in books and movies, has already had the effect of unloosing prosecutors and police in a misguided crusade to protect public morals by denying to those who are incapable of personal sexual relations the tawdry pleasure of sex at second hand. There is no indication that anyone in public office is interested in giving effect to the conviction of the Sex Information and Education Council of the U.S. that "the best protection of young people against possible harm by pornography is by providing sufficient sex information of high calibre at appropriate times in their life cycles to satisfy the natural curiosity which may lead them to pornography" (statement to the Commission on Obscenity and Pornography, April 1970).

I am personally opposed to any kind of censorship affecting adults' rights to read and view whatever they wish.*

---

would increase the threat to our social order as well as to our moral principles. Alexis de Tocqueville, observing America more than a century ago, wrote: 'America is great because she is good—and if America ceases to be good, America will cease to be great.' We all hold the responsibility for keeping America a good country. American morality is not to be trifled with. The Commission on Obscenity and Pornography has performed a disservice and I totally reject its report."

* See my chapter on "Sex, Religion and Censorship" in *Censorship and Freedom of Expression* (ed. Clor, Harry M.). As I make clear there and later in this book, I do not condone the values of pornography. Nor am I opposed to restraints on the sale of pornography to minors. The statement of the Sex Information and Education Council quoted above draws attention very firmly to the possible effects of distorted sexual values on children who are still in the process of forming their sexual identities.

The possibility that obscenity laws will be used to restrict freedom of speech is by no means to be dismissed. In 1970 the military regime in Brazil intimidated the press from protesting the use of torture through a decree ostensibly controlling "licentious publications" (*Commonweal,* April 24, 1970). In this country the attempt of extreme right-wing groups (with some success) to campaign against sex education as a "Communist plot" is indicative of the close association between political reaction and sexual repression. It was no mere accident that a four-letter word became the symbol of the Free Speech movement at Berkeley in 1968.

Popular appeal to prurient anti-sexualism in our culture is an effective way of distracting attention from the real evils of society. "This society is obscene," writes Herbert Marcuse (1969), "in producing and indecently exposing a stifling abundance of wares while depriving its victims abroad of the necessities of life; obscene in stuffing itself and its garbage cans while poisoning and burning the scarce foodstuffs in the fields of its aggression; obscene in the words and smiles of its politicians and entertainers; in its prayers, in its ignorance, and in the wisdom of its kept intellectuals. . . . Obscene is not the picture of a naked woman who exposes her pubic hair, but that of a fully clad general who exposes his medals rewarded in a war of aggression; obscene is not the ritual of the Hippies but the declaration of a high dignitary of the Church that war is necessary for peace" (pp. 7–8).

A similar protest, in the name of religion, was made at the time of the civil rights confrontation in Birmingham, Alabama: "For Christians the truly obscene ought not to be slick-paper nudity, nor the vulgarities of dirty old or young literati, nor even 'weirdo' films showing transvestite orgies or male genitalia. What is obscene is that material, whether sexual or not, that has as its basic motivation and purpose the degradation, debasement and dehumanizing of persons. The dirtiest word in the English language is not 'fuck' or 'shit' in the mouth of a tragic shaman [Lenny Bruce], but the word 'NIGGER' from the sneering lips of a Bull Connor" (Moody, 1965).

One of the most profound sources of difficulty in reaching a positive and coherent understanding of one's sexuality continues to be our society's irrational condemnation of masturbation. A Kinsey Institute report in 1973 stated that nearly half the population of the United States still disapproves of the practice. As a result, while nine out of ten college men masturbate (Kinsey, 1948), a significant number are anxious and ill at ease about it. Not so long ago one study of the sex histories of college students showed several suffering from fear of losing their hair, breaking out in acne, going blind or approaching insanity because they masturbated (Kronhausen and Kronhausen, 1960). A survey of postgraduate students conducted in the seventies reported that 40 percent of the males harbored guilt feelings over masturbation (Greenberg and Archambault, 1973).

The fact is that masturbation is a common phase of early human development, part of the natural infantile exploration and enjoyment of the body and better described as "self-discovery" than as "self-abuse." The Group for the Advancement of Psychiatry in its report entitled *Sex and the College Student* stated that in adolescence "in addition to the simple discharge of sexual tension, masturbation serves such purposes as the reduction of anxiety, expression of hostility, fantasying of sexual experimentation, assertion of sexual identity in anticipation or recall" (Eddy, 1966, p. 88). Masturbation is never a cause of emotional illness. Obsessive masturbation in adulthood which interferes with other responsibilities may be symptomatic of psychological problems. Some adolescents masturbate as an escape from social problems or personal relations; in such cases it is not the act of masturbation but the underlying problem that needs attention. Far from being a contributor to later sexual problems, masturbation is a positive aid in preparation for intercourse (Kinsey, 1948, 1953). As Stekel (1950) pointed out, if the "awful habit" were as harmful as ignorant crusaders have maintained, the majority of the human race would be hospitalized.

Those who warn students against "excessive" masturbation merely substitute a new and equally ill-founded anxiety for an old one, since what is "excessive" remains unknown to the troubled person. Physical damage from masturbation is, in fact, an impossibility. The capacity for further arousal is exhausted long before any harm can be done to the system. Frequent ejaculation does not affect the male's capacity for later sexual activity or his fertility, since sperm and semen are continually produced by the testicles, seminal vesicles and prostate. There is no evidence to support the widely held myth that masturbation adversely affects academic or athletic performance (Kinsey, 1948; Johnson, 1968). It may, on the contrary, help by reducing unnecessary tension. It is surely better for a person to masturbate and sleep soundly than to spend a restless night fighting off a need for sexual release.

The number of women who masturbate is less than the number of men (Kinsey, 1953). Two recent studies have reported a figure as high as two out of three among college women (Greenberg and Archambault, 1973; Abramson, 1973) but others (Kaats and Davis, 1972) put the percentage much lower. Bardwick (1971) thinks the differential may be due to the fact that the male organs are external and more easily stimulated in childhood and adolescence.

But Schaefer (1973) suggests that the persistence of hesitation and anxiety about masturbation by women is due to the difficulty women have, in our culture, in accepting their physical sexuality as good in itself: "Masturbation entails a personal admission of, and responsibility for, one's sexual feelings. Participation in interpersonal sex is rationalized on many grounds—love, passion, dating and popularity, marriage, pleasing one's partner, wifely duty, etc. —but masturbation can be considered only as the individual's direct expression of immediate sexual feelings" (pp. 88–89).

Philip and Lorna Sarrel * have found that many women they have talked with at Yale are confused about masturbation. Contemporary student expectations put them under pressure to engage in masturbation, but their own value systems make it difficult to do so. It is obviously as undesirable for anyone to feel she *must* masturbate to conform to an external demand as it is for her to feel she should not. Those whose upbringing has instilled a deep objection to this form of sexual expression can only follow their personal convictions and should not feel in any way sexually inadequate for abstaining. But many counselors believe that masturbation can be an important means of sexual self-discovery and growth for a woman who has no sense of guilt about it. Schaefer (1973) specifically describes masturbation as a "type of therapy" which will reduce the likelihood of unresponsiveness in later coitus, and blames "prohibitions against all manner of sexual self-exploration and education" (p. 105) for the failure of many women to avail themselves of this experience.

Masturbation does have one obvious limitation—it is a solitary activity (though not "the solitary vice"). Dr.

* Personal communication.

Krankheit, in that altogether unsubtle spoof on pornography, *Candy,* argues that heterosexual love is the root of all neurosis and advocates masturbation as "the only sex-mode that permits complete fulfillment and mental health." But, on the contrary, sex isolated from personal relationships is at best a temporary substitute. "Repeated masturbation is a very lonely business," writes Sherfey (1972). "I cannot imagine a single human being, short of those most disturbed or isolated from his fellows, who would prefer masturbation, however intense the orgasms, over the sharing warmth of sexual relations, however mild the orgasms, with a loved one" (p. 162).

Two participants in a discussion of "Single Girls and Sex" remarked: "It was really boring because I was by myself and there was nobody there. . . ." "I have tremendous guilt about masturbation. . . . A shame about not having a partner" (Gould, 1971). The reason for this dissatisfaction, suggests Gordon (1968), is that while masturbation is a key "unification experience" in which mind and body coalesce and the person is momentarily integrated, the unification is limited to the individual self and does not (as in intercourse) include unity with others. Schaefer (1973) quotes the comments of two of the women in her sample which confirm this insight:

I did it a lot even during my marriage because the funny thing was that the climax itself was much more satisfying, much greater than being with a guy. I felt terrible afterward, sick and then depressed because then you're alone and a lot of fun of sex is being with someone.

Part of the reason I feel badly is that I know that masturbation keeps me in a self-sufficient system, which is my problem (p. 100).

Despite modern knowledge masturbation remains an even more sensitive subject for discussion between parents and children than intercourse. Mothers still usually make it very plain to small children that, while other bodily pleasures of all kinds are to be enjoyed, the genitals are to be left alone. The impression of disapproval and disgust is, of course, strengthened by the young child's inability to make a clear distinction between the genitals and the anus from which "dirty" feces come. Parents indicate obvious anxiety and inappropriate curiosity whenever they suspect adolescents of masturbating. The public reaction to Philip Roth's novel *Portnoy's Complaint* indicated that a sensitive nerve had been touched, and I suspect that it was in part the fact that Jeanne masturbates in *Last Tango in Paris* that gained it an X rating.

It is easy to be critical of parents who fail to provide adequate sex education and to erase the irrational sense of guilt about masturbation. But it is worth remembering that the parents of this generation received even less effective sex education. When today's fathers were boys the official handbook of the Boy Scouts of America stated that "in the body of every boy who has reached his teens, the Creator of the universe has sown a very important fluid. This fluid is the most wonderful material in all the physical world. Some parts of it find their way into the blood, and through the blood give tone to the muscles, power to the brain, and strength to the nerves. This fluid is the sex fluid. . . . Any habit which a boy has that causes this fluid to be discharged from his body tends to weaken his strength, to make him less able to resist disease, and often unfortunately fastens upon him habits which later in life can be broken only with great difficulty" (Gordon, 1968, p. 24). As late as 1940 a candidate for admission to the Naval

Academy at Annapolis was rejected if the examining surgeon found "evidence of masturbation" (whatever that was).

Within recent times as influential an exponent of male machismo as Norman Mailer (1971) has written: "I think masturbation is bad . . . masturbation cripples people. It doesn't cripple them altogether, but it turns them askew, it sets up a bad and often enduring tension. . . . Anybody who spends his adolescence masturbating, generally enters his young manhood with no sense of being a man. . . . The ultimate direction of masturbation always has to be insanity" (pp. 135–36). Mailer emphasizes that it is the lack of personal challenge that he finds unmanly in masturbation, in contrast to the demands of intercourse. He is right in claiming that the substitution of masturbation for *all* interpersonal sexual relationships in adulthood may be symptomatic of immaturity. But he fails to recognize that intercourse may not always be either possible or appropriate. If every time somebody felt the need for relief he (or she) had to utilize a female (or male) body there would be a great deal more coercive and destructive sexual activity. Mailer totally ignores the possibility, noted by a student writer, that "honest masturbation is a lot healthier than a dishonest lay."

It is common to blame Western religion for the cultural abhorrence of masturbation. The Old Testament story of Onan (Genesis 38) has been the source of Christian* teaching that God punishes those who "spill their seed on the ground"—though it is now generally accepted that Onan

---

* In classical Jewish thought other biblical texts were also important as a basis for rabbinic repudiation of *hash-hatat zera,* destruction of seed or improper seminal emission (Feldman, 1968). The Code of Jewish Law (Ganzfield, 1961) still binding on Orthodox Jews treats the "discharge of semen in vain" as the gravest sin mentioned in the Torah (Chapter 151).

was in fact practicing *coitus interruptus* by withdrawing before ejaculation and therefore failing to fulfill his social duty to impregnate the widow of his brother. It was this, rather than the mere loss of semen that was condemned (Cole, 1959). (Maybe Onan was an early exponent of the relation of sex and love, refusing to have coitus with a woman he didn't particularly like!) The medieval Church regarded masturbation as a more serious sin than fornication, adultery or rape (Bailey, 1959)—perhaps because it was the sexual temptation to which monastic clergy were most liable and because of what Bailey calls the "superstitious reverence for semen" of the Middle Ages. It is also true that Catholic moral theologians still teach that it is sinful and must be controlled, confessed and eventually overcome (Dedek, 1971; O'Neil and Donovan, 1968).

But the responsibility for the unhealthy situation is at least as much that of the medical profession. It was a Swiss physician, Tissot, who first (in 1758) gave spurious support to religious teaching in his *Onanism: a treatise on the disorders produced by masturbation*. Respected medical men throughout the nineteenth century attributed conditions such as impotence and insanity to masturbation. Authorities like Sigmund Freud and Havelock Ellis even in the twentieth century expressed great concern about the implications of autoeroticism after adolescence. In the 1920s manufacturers of medical equipment were still advertising complicated (and very painful) devices to be fitted on boys and girls to prevent them from masturbating (Schwarz, 1973). Comfort (1968) in a chapter called "The Rise and Fall of Self-Abuse" states that this pseudomedical nonsense died out after the publication of the Kinsey studies; but Masters and Johnson (1968) found that they were still frequently being asked by doctors at professional meetings whether masturbation caused insanity.

If masturbation were accepted as a normal phenomenon of adolescence, no more reprehensible than wet dreams for boys or the beginning of menstruation for girls, a great deal of anxiety and suffering would be avoided. To condemn it as wicked or sinful is as stupid as to punish a baby for crying when it is hungry or a child for climbing trees. It is part of healthy sexual experience, and in adulthood it may be an appropriate alternative when the person has no suitable sexual partner. It only leads to undesirable consequences when it is associated with guilt and fear based on ignorance or irrational dogmatism. But such anxieties and prejudices are so ingrained in our culture that knowledge of the facts may not easily put an end to them, and emotional scars can result from masturbation if it runs contrary to deeply held convictions. Those who continue to have feelings of self-condemnation cannot simply ignore their conscience: they should try to avoid the practice at least until they see it in a different light.

All these illustrations make clear how deeply uncertain our society is about sexuality, and it is no wonder that college students start with a built-in problem in trying to arrive at a rational sexual standard. Some inevitably remain falsely inhibited and insecure in their sexual relations. Others react and repudiate all restraints. Very few are unaffected by the ambiguity of our culture. The Group for the Advancement of Psychiatry (1968) has stated the problem well: "No one whose childhood was lived in the context of a prohibitive morality can be really free of its legacy of sexual guilt. The nature of the dilemma determines the standard variations of adolescent efforts at solution of the problem: rebellion against sexual ethics and denial of conscience; early dependent marriage; early marriage with withdrawal from the socio-economic struggle; repudiation of sexual prohibitions in good faith and with sincerity but with unavoidable unconscious guilt; subordination of sex strong repression of sexuality, with the likelihood of subsequent mental or emotional disorder. The attitudes of middle-class culture make it very nearly impossible for adolescents to employ, in a healthy way, the alternatives to to, and contamination of sex with, competitive goals; or such modes of behavior, namely, masturbation or sexual intimacies with the opposite sex appropriate to the individual's age and degree of emotional maturity" (pp. 43–44).

Despite these contradictions, it is a mistake to dismiss our society's sexual attitudes as beyond hope of improvement. Changes in sexual patterns are taking place and a more realistic and honest acceptance of sexuality is developing. The fact that today's students live in an age of rapid social change does not make the task of sorting out the contradictions of one's sexual heritage any easier. But the years on campus offer a challenge and a unique opportunity to establish personally coherent sexual values.

CHAPTER II

Values on Campus

"I think that sex is just one of the greatest pleasures of life, and that your body is ready for it and needs it at the age of puberty, be it ten or thirteen or fifteen, and that when the body needs it you should accommodate the body's needs and your own desires." Underlying this statement, made to me by a student in a recording for a film-strip (Hettlinger, 1969), is the widespread view that sex is a simple physical need that ought to be satisfied without concern over questions of ethics or social convention. A common analogy is drawn between sex and eating: both are responses to instinctual needs, and it is as absurd (and dangerous) to deny ourselves sex as it is to deny ourselves food. A failure to satisfy the sexual urge, it is frequently supposed, will lead to emotional damage and to sexual inadequacy in adulthood. Ellis (1963) has said dogmatically that "when a young man does, for any considerable period of time, remain even moderately (not to mention completely) abstinent, there is every reason to believe that he may do himself considerable harm and that he is practically never likely to do himself any good" (p. 14).

If this is the case a discussion of values is irrelevant in a book on sex: for values imply some criteria by which to determine when and how sexuality should be expressed. If sex is a physical need to which one should respond immediately the only "value" to be considered is that of satisfying the demands of the body.

If we look more closely at the analogy, however, it turns out to be far from conclusive. While one cannot live without eating anything, one can live very well without eating *some* things: indeed abstention from certain foods is essential to the life of many people, and the human system adapts without any ill effects to dietary restrictions or other situations when particular foods are unavailable. We do not think the immediate satisfaction of physical hunger a good thing in all circumstances. An alcoholic or a member of a group with limited supplies who fails to control an intense desire for drink or food is not applauded. Equally, even if it is true (and the fact has not been demonstrated) that abstinence from *all* forms of sexual release is necessarily harmful, it does not follow that abstinence from *some* forms of sexual release is harmful. A conscious choice, based on reasonable principles, to abstain from intercourse and to be satisfied temporarily with petting or masturbation may be entirely healthy.

Masters (1968) has pointed out that "there must be countless lifetime celibates who have not become neurotic." *The Playboy Advisor*, in reply to a query from two anxious readers, put it this way:

Abstinence, as such, is neither good nor bad for the health. What does affect the individual's well-being are the circumstances of, and the motivations for, his abstention. Kinsey points out that men who are physically incapacitated, natively low in sex drive, sexually unawakened in their early years or separated from their usual sources of sexual stimulation can abstain indefinitely without appreciable harm. Even when these conditions do not prevail, if the motivation for abstention is conscious and rational, no harm will be done (*Playboy*, November 1967).

The studies of Ardrey (1966), Lorenz (1967) and Morris (1967) have been interpreted by many as giving support to the view that instincts must inevitably exert a decisive power in human relationships. Beneath the surface gloss, according to Morris, the naked ape is "still very much a primate" subject to the irresistible urges of raw animal need. Ardrey takes it as axiomatic that human beings are largely controlled by animal instinct and bound to be aggressive. These reminders of the fragility of human societies and the danger that the quality of our relationships may be debased by less than human behavior are timely. But they should not be taken to mean that sexual values are unimportant, or that we can remain human beings and abandon ourselves unthinkingly to the satisfaction of our physical needs. A movie called *The Fear* was promoted by an ad showing a man apparently raping a woman, with the caption: "There are hungers no man can deny." But few of us think for a moment that the analogy holds in this case. It must be remembered that the very concept of "instinct" (at least in man) as an inherent disposition or impulse which determines behavior and is beyond conscious control is repudiated by many responsible scientists (Ashley Montagu, 1968).

Lorenz, while stressing the value of aggression or initiative in man, has complained of the misinterpretation that attributes to him the view that man is controlled by instinct: "I tried to show the existence of internal forces that man must know in order to master. I said that reason could conquer aggression." And in a specific reference to the sexual implications of his theories Lorenz warned that taking "the theoreticians of complete sexual promiscuity" at their word would involve enormous damage to human culture (*The New York Times Magazine*, July 5, 1970). For Lorenz the absolutely new and critical factor in the human situation is the appearance of language, the possibility of a cumulative tradition or culture, and "the greatest gift of all, rational responsible morality," which gives man the power to control his animal inheritance (1967, p. 232).

Man is indeed an animal, and the ethologists are right to remind us that a recognition of that fact is vital if human existence is to be preserved. But man is an animal whose physical needs have been given more than purely physical significance. Sex in particular has come to have emotional and social associations that are absent from other activities, such as eating.* Even eating is surrounded by many social customs which, in normal civilized circumstances, involve considerable restraints on the immediate satisfaction of hunger. But sex is even more deeply associated with cultural expectations since, except for masturbation, it always involves another person. In a unique sense this particular physical urge has been transformed in the course of human history.

The role played in human sexuality by cultural development makes it impossible to hide behind any simple identification of sex and hunger, and makes responsible decisions about values unavoidable. "Because all complex human behavior is heavily dependent upon cortical pro-

---

* This is the point that Theodor Reik (1957) ignored in his rigid distinction between sex and love. He was obviously right in questioning a simplistic identification of the two terms. We do have sexual experiences with people we do not love, and we all love people with whom we have no (genital) sexual relationship. But in human culture sex does have emotional and volitional associations that are absent from other physical activities. Despite Reik's prophecy it is unlikely that in the near future we shall think of libido "in chemical terms only."

cesses it is automatically open to modification through the influences of previous experience. This explains why, in human beings more than in any other species, sexuality is structured and patterned by learning" (Ford and Beach, 1951, p. 259). As Arieti (1972) points out, "When an animal reacts to hunger, thirst, sexual desire, it does not choose; it responds. It has no alternative; it has to follow the urge. Although these animal functions are motivated, they are not willed and do not imply conscious selection. Can a man revert to the stage of simple appetite? Only in extreme rare cases, the existence of which are doubted: the cases of so-called irresistible impulses. These cases occur only in conditions of severe pathology, mental illness, or early infancy" (pp. 36–37).

Studies of the development of moral reasoning (Piaget, 1932; Kohlberg, 1964; Maddock, 1972; O'Connor and Wrightsman, 1972) suggest that people pass through several stages in the process of achieving mature, integrated ethical standards. At first a child accepts the distinction between right and wrong simply in terms of the physical consequences associated with the words. That is good which results in pleasurable experience; that is bad which is associated with pain, punishment or parental disapproval. Authority figures are obeyed and their edicts followed without any awareness of principles or any sense of a general moral order. Purely pragmatic and hedonistic interests are at work.

At a second level the expectations and approval of the group (initially the family) become significant factors, sometimes outweighing the values of personal pleasure. Thus immediate private advantage may be subordinated to the sense of loyalty to others and to the satisfaction of approval by society. Rules are obeyed for their own sake in the interests of the common good. Only at a third level of maturity, at what Kohlberg calls the "postconventional" stage, is the ideal of personal value embraced and the possibility affirmed of challenging social definitions of right and wrong in the name of one's own understanding of good and evil. While this is theoretically the foundation of our society it is by no means embraced by all. The opposition to the Vietnam war represented a significant assertion of postconventional moral judgment by many; but a large proportion of the population still give loyalty to "my country—right or wrong." In sexual matters the great majority of adults still feel it important to uphold the traditional ideal of premarital chastity even though many of them did not practice it themselves.*

The transition from conventional moral reasoning to postconventional independence takes place during adolescence and may often only be fully achieved during the years at college. But it does not represent the full development of the human capacity for ethical maturity. This comes only when a person is able to define the right in terms of self-chosen moral principles based on universal applicability and logical consistency. This involves more than the acceptance of a set of laws or rules of even the most demanding kind (such as the Ten Commandments). It is a decision of conscience to live, as far as possible, by an ideal such as that of Kant (always treat another person as an end, not only as a means: act on that maxim which you would will to become a universal law) or of the Sermon on the Mount (love your neighbor as yourself: always treat others as you would like them to treat you).

The achievement of postconventional morality should surely be the concern of any mature person, and most students *claim* to have achieved independence from the purely traditional standards of society. But I suspect that

---

* Kinsey (1953) found that the major change in sexual behavior (as distinct from sexual ideals) came with the generation which went to college immediately after the *first* World War.

sexual behavior on campus is more often less free of convention than it appears. Rather than being based on independent values it frequently seems to be motivated by a continuing need to reject traditional mores. It continues to be an extension of the necessary adolescent celebration of escape from the confines of establishment anti-sexualism, rather than a mature and considered pattern based on reflection and critical judgment.

Not infrequently, submission to the authority of parents or church is replaced by tutelage to a new, dogmatic ideal of sexual expertise. For the dedicated pursuit of "organ grinding" can be as destructive of personal freedom and of human relationships as the most rigid Victorianism. One experienced psychiatrist has stated: "Some of the people whom I knew who had great, vivid, violent orgastic potency could not fit into any psychiatric description of an emotionally mature person in relationship with other people" (Granatir, 1968). Masters (1968) has warned that "the greatest mistake a male can make is to feel that because he has a certain amount of technical competence, he is an effective sexual entity." Schaefer (1973) makes it clear that the same is true for a female: "The ability to experience orgasm through heterosexual sex does not necessarily ensure an ability to achieve warm and satisfying heterosexual relationships and vice versa" (p. 17).

Conflict between adolescents and their parents very frequently focuses on the question of sexual behavior because the necessary task of asserting one's own individuality against the family requires that one's freedom as a sexual person be affirmed. According to Storr (1968) self-esteem is *chiefly* rooted in sexuality:

A confident belief in one's own masculinity or femininity is a fundamental part of human identity. . . . The normal person, if such exists, constantly renews a sense of value through loving and being loved; and the object of physical passion is thus not only a means whereby the drive of sexuality can be expressed and assuaged, but also a vital source of self-esteem. We cannot escape our physical natures; and a proper pride in oneself as a human being is rooted in the body through which love is given and taken (pp. 68–69).

Interference by parents in the freedom to engage in sexual activity can easily appear to be an infringement on the right to independence. But at a deeper level adolescence means the re-ordering of the infantile sexual relationship to one's parents. It has been said that you can only fall in love with a girl (or boy) when you fall out of love with your mother (or father). And unconsciously the repudiation of parental sexual standards involves a rift between the generations that it is almost impossible to handle on a rational level. It is therefore inevitable that rebellion against adult ideals of chastity can take on something of the quality of a crusade, and independence and freedom seem to be synonymous with unrestrained sexuality. But this is surely a fallacy. Rebellion for its own sake can be a conformity as rigid as unquestioning obedience to authority. To sleep around just because the adult world says it is forbidden is no more a truly mature thing to do than it is to preserve your virginity just because your mother told you to. True freedom is the capacity to develop one's own individual values as a sexual being, questioning what is erroneous in the standards of the past, but embracing whatever wisdom the experience of others conveys.*

* Personally I believe that the perpetuation of rules governing private sexual behavior on campus tends to encourage immaturity. Many sexual adventures are motivated by a need to assert self-identity against the authority figures of college administrators *in loco parentis*. If this motive

Most people have in the past eventually worked out a reasonable accommodation between their parents' values and their own life styles. Reiss (1967) found that two out of three college students saw their sexual *standards* as similar to those of their parents—though a large proportion felt guilt about their sexual *behavior*. He also found that as people came to assume the responsibilities of marriage and family their standards became more conservative: the degree of permissiveness was markedly lower among married than among unmarried adults, and lower yet among parents with teenaged children. But Reiss's study was conducted ten years ago, and two developments in the past decade make it less likely that today's students will eventually adopt their parents' standards.

First, those who (understandably) dismiss the moral authority of a society that bombed Hanoi and Cambodia, failed to distinguish between the seriousness of marijuana and heroin and produced the Watergate scandals are more likely to reject the sexual mores of their parents. "Once you have taken drugs and broken that rule, it's easier to break all the others," commented one college senior.

Second, there has been a significant new development separating the generations since about 1965. Up to that time the number of male students engaging in intercourse (while, as we shall see, not as high as is popularly assumed) was much greater than the number of women students doing so. But parental standards, while technically uniform, were often perceived as permitting much more liberty for men to experiment. The possibility of an accommodation between the two was therefore open. During the past decade there has been a marked increase in the per-

were defused and personal sexual freedom recognized, I think more students would be ready to learn from the experience and ideas of faculty members and administrators (Hettlinger, 1972).

centage of women engaging in intercourse at college (Davis, 1971), but there is little evidence of a similar modification of parental attitudes towards the sexual freedom of their daughters. Not only do parents not communicate any expectation that their female children will engage in intercourse; they frequently refuse to face or discuss the fact that they have done so when it is obviously the case.

One recent study of the attitudes of unmarried upperclass women at the University of Oregon and of their mothers found them so far apart on the specific issue of premarital intercourse that the author argued that attempts at communication on the subject would exacerbate rather than alleviate generational conflict (LoPiccolo, 1973). Many women tell me that their fathers find it impossible to imagine their involvement in any sexual experience, and one student who was planning to live with her male friend while they attended graduate school at the same institution found that her parents simply failed to acknowledge the situation, despite her broad hints. In such circumstances the possibility remains that sex on campus may be an expression of revolt rather than based on consistent principle.

*   *   *

If freedom from, rather than reaction to, parental or other traditional authorities is difficult to achieve, submission to new but equally binding external standards is difficult to avoid. The peer group plays a valuable role in providing support for the individual in the necessary adolescent process of establishing personal independence. But it can, in its turn, be a threat to the development of mature standards. There is a persuasive pressure towards uniformity and against individual judgment on every campus. Loss of virginity is represented as the norm and the (considerable) minority who prefer to delay the experience of intercourse are often made to feel inadequate. One female student confided to a counselor that her virginity was such a burden to her that: "On a trip to Greece, I found any old Greek and did it so it wouldn't be an issue any more." Another woman reported, "It isn't just the boys who pressure you into bed, but it's the other girls. Not that they say anything, but just by being around them I feel like some kind of nut" (Steinem, 1972).

The authority of campus experts has been given new status and apparently objective support in recent years. A group of sexual prophets, as unqualified in their dogmatism as the religious teachers of the past, now assure the doubtful that sexual restraints are demonstrably ridiculous and orgasmic pleasure the universal test of maturity. Thus Ellis (1969) states: "Among enlightened and educated young people today, I would call the preservation of virginity before marriage an overt display of arrant masochism." A widely read sex guide contains the assertion that "if marriage is not possible (for any number of reasons), then sex without marriage is the only alternative. (*No sex is so stupid it is not even worth considering as a possibility.*)" (Reuben, 1969, pp. 107–8).*

The result is a reversed sexual anxiety, a guilt about feeling guilty, a new dogmatism to which many subscribe because of external pressure. There is a new puritanism of the sexually emancipated which can just as easily discourage honest and independent thinking. "Sin," writes Rollo May (1969), "used to mean giving in to one's sexual desires; it now means not having full sexual expression. Our contemporary puritan holds that it is immoral *not* to express your libido. . . . A woman used to be guilty if she went to bed with a man, now she feels vaguely guilty if

---

* The emphasis is mine. By "sex" Reuben specifically means intercourse.

after a certain number of dates she still refrains" (pp. 45–46).

The results can be tragic for those whose preference or persuasion or physical qualities exclude them from the experiences that the more vocal libertarians take for granted. A graduate student in a letter to *Sexual Behavior* (March, 1972) complained that magazines like *Playboy* are "more frustrating than helpful because they give the impression that everybody but me has a good, active sexual life" and declared that his constant obsession with the problem of his own virginity had contributed to a difficult time in college. "What has the so-called sexual revolution meant for those too homely, too disagreeable, too sheltered, or too inhibited to participate in the sexual economy?" asked Christopher Jencks (1964). "My guess is that they are the real losers as campus mores change. For every suicide brought on by sexual intercourse, there are probably a dozen precipitated by lack of dates; for every psychiatric patient burdened with an unwanted marriage or an unforgotten abortion, there are probably two suffering from the absence of invitations to such disasters."

While figures for intercourse on campus are notoriously hard to estimate because of great variations between different institutions depending on their location and cultural background, they are lower than many students assume. On a large midwestern state university the actual percentage of campus virgins was underestimated by 78 percent of the women interviewed (Jackson and Potkay, 1973). A reasonable estimate, based on recent studies,* is that on a national average about 65 percent of today's male college students engage in coitus and about 50 percent of to-

---

* Luckey and Nass, 1969; Bell and Chaskes, 1970; Christensen and Gregg, 1970; Kaats and Davis, 1970; Davis, 1971; Robinson et al., 1972; Freedman and Lozoff, 1972; Jackson and Potkay, 1973; Arafat and Yorburg, 1973a.

day's college women. All in all the picture is *not* one in which students universally regard the question of virginity as closed. Whether an individual's decision is to engage in intercourse or not should be based on responsible consideration of the issues involved and the values he or she wants to preserve, *not* on a sense of inevitability artificially produced by misinformation about statistics, or on the loudly touted myth of the disappearing virgin. One out of every three men and one out of every two women on campus today will probably fall in that category at graduation.

Virginity or non-virginity, however, is not the only issue of importance. What is more significant is the quality of sexual intimacy; and here again the student, particularly the freshman, is likely to be influenced by the popular impression that on campus "anything goes." Unfortunately this assumption vitiates several widely read studies of student sexual activity. By failing to distinguish between intercourse in a purely casual situation and its occurrence as an expression of affection and commitment, they succeed in giving an unbalanced picture of the moral climate on campuses. A survey carried out by Daniel Yankelovich Inc. (1972) concluded that in recent years there had been a major change in sexual morality because "casual premarital sexual relations" had increased. A book by the sociologist Vance Packard had the significant title *The Sexual Wilderness* (1968); but, while it contained some valuable material, it too gave a false impression of moral irresponsibility by treating all acts of intercourse outside of marriage as equally promiscuous. Packard exclaimed in dismay at the discovery that 58 percent of American college males and 43 percent of American college women admitted to coital experience. But a careful reading of his figures shows than only 30 percent of the males and only 7 percent of the females had ever engaged in a "one night affair involving coitus," and he admitted that the figure for promiscuity among college women was "practically insignificant" since most of the 7 percent came from one university in New York City.

It is difficult to know what to make of those who thus exaggerate the degree of irresponsible sex on campus. One Catholic college chaplain suggested that "the image of large numbers of college students 'sleeping around,' indiscriminately indulging in sex for kicks and pleasure without any concern for consequences or permanence, appears to reflect more the frustrated yearnings of writers and readers than it does actual campus life" (Walsh, 1967). A British writer has put it more bluntly. The older generation, he suggests, have "an almost obscene obsession with the sexuality of the young . . . prompted by envious rancour and a bullying intention to interfere" (MacInnes, 1963).

But whatever the reason, reports on student sexual behavior that suggest a morass of indulgence can obviously have the effect of pressuring some people into casual sex they do not really want because they perceive it to be expected of them at college. That it is a false, or at least an oversimplified, impression is clear. Kinsey (1948) found, for example, that a much smaller percentage of students ever visited a prostitute than was the case among the less educated groups, and students almost always find the experience degrading. The Katz study (1968) concluded that "sexual intimacy seems to take place in the context of a relationship that is serious rather than casual" (p. 56). The number of male and female students having their first coital experience in a non-committed relationship or having coitus with more than one person *declined* significantly in the midwestern United States between 1958 and 1968 (Christensen and Gregg, 1970).

Vreeland (1972), who studied the dating patterns of

Harvard men, comparing their interests in 1960 and 1970, found that while the desire for sexual intimacy remained constant, and the likelihood that it would include intercourse increased, companionship was more highly rated than sexual conquest. "Our evidence does not suggest the sexual revolution that has been publicized," she writes. "The Harvard men of the '70s are much more interested in the *companion* pattern of dating, characterized by an intense emotional relationship with a woman that, although containing a sexual component, is similar to a same-sex peer relationship. Girls are sought as friends in their own right rather than partners for recreation or status achievements. . . . Students today date more frequently and become more committed to one woman than did their counterparts of the 1960s . . . we found less evidence of unbridled promiscuity than a relaxation of restrictions on sexual intercourse for couples involved in a more or less stable relationship." Arafat and Yorburg (1973a), who questioned several hundred female students using drugs in 1970–71, reported that "the modal sexual pattern even among heavy drug users is that of fidelity to a single partner at any time . . . the promiscuity pattern is a minority pattern among drug users in our study."

The point of all this is not to argue for the adoption of a less permissive set of values because most students are less casual in their sexual behavior than their image suggests. To do that would be to attempt to impose another statistical tyranny. Nor am I denying that there is a good deal of impersonal and exploitative sex on campus. The aggressive obsession with sexual conquest represented by Jonathan and Sandy in the movie *Carnal Knowledge* was a caricature—but a caricature of an attitude one frequently encounters among students. What I am urging is the importance of each individual's establishing his or her own personal, coherent, rational basis for sexual behavior without being pressured by a need to comply with any dogmatic authority, old or new, or with any supposed uniform values characteristic of the student community.

*   *   *

Another barrier to the establishment of mature values is overconcern with measurable sexual behavior. Figures and percentages can undoubtedly contribute enormously to freedom from false fears and unnecessary guilt. To know that 95 percent of all males masturbate, or that the great majority of women are capable of enjoying orgasm, or that 5 percent of the population is homosexual, can be truly liberating. I do not want in any way to question the value of such studies as those of Kinsey and of Masters and Johnson. Accurate factual information about sexual practices of various people, and about the physiology of sexual response, is essential. Unfortunately some treatments of the ethical and personal aspects of the subject have been guilty of gross neglect of the scientific findings. But the simple fact that coitus and orgasm are relatively clear identifiable experiences makes these the natural criteria for statistical measurement, and as a result these particular elements of human sexuality tend to be isolated from the whole gamut of personal relationships. Kinsey, for example, in listing the number of sexual "outlets" (a peculiarly masculine phrase) experienced by different people drew no statistical distinction between an orgasm resulting from intercourse with a farm animal or one enjoyed in the context of a deeply human love-relationship. The result is a distorted focusing of attention on sex as a target-oriented activity. The ease with which we identify "sex" and coitus in ordinary speech illustrates the trend. We can say, quite absurdly, of a couple who are in love and enjoying every form of intimacy short of intercourse that they are *not* "having sex together."

The authors of the major research works were themselves quite aware of the limitations of their treatment of sexuality. Kinsey (1948) repeatedly pointed out that he had not identified *the* American sexual pattern and after a full statement of the arguments pro and con premarital intercourse concluded with this warning: "The resolution of these conflicting claims can come only through some recognition that certain of these problems lie in areas which belong to the biologic, psychologic, and social sciences, while others are moral problems which the student of moral philosophies most solve" (1953, p. 309).

Masters and Johnson (1968) have freely acknowledged that their work was intentionally restricted to the physical aspects of sexuality and that the *why* of sexual response is far more important than the *what*. In an article, "A Defense of Love and Morality" (*McCalls,* November 1966), they stressed that sex as a physical phenomenon is only a small part of sexuality. But popular interpretation has all too often assumed that factual research has settled, or made irrelevant, questions of personal judgment: and as a result instead of students working out their own standards with honesty and consistency they can easily fall into an uncritical and oversimplified search for the perfect orgasm, ignoring the psychological, social and ethical issues that are inseparable from *human* sexuality.

A particular problem arises for many women as a byproduct of the new understanding of female sexuality. The search for what has been called "the liberated orgasm" (Seaman, 1972) can turn out to be yet another compulsive obsession. The impression that all women who fail to enjoy multiple orgasms are sexually inadequate can be as serious a barrier to the development of independent values as the older assumption that all women who enjoyed sex were "nymphomaniacs." * "The sexual revolution—liberated orgastic women, groupies, communal lovemaking, homosexuality—has made us feel that we must be able to have sex with impunity, without anxiety, under any conditions and with anyone, or we're uptight freaks. These alienating, inhuman expectations are no less destructive or degrading than the Victorian puritanism we all so proudly rejected" (*Our Bodies, Our Selves,* 1973, p. 23).

Two women participants in a discussion expressed their anxieties thus:

Sara: I will tell you something that I feel is unacceptable. Right now there is a lot of pressure on women to function well sexually. People feel it is unacceptable for a woman not to be able to have an orgasm because of all the literature and all the studies that are going on. That makes me nervous. That bothers me because it is in such contradiction to the way I was raised. It is like telling a girl to switch all of a sudden. After not being allowed to, you are *supposed* to perform, and not just perform but to enjoy yourself. That is very hard for me. I am having some problems in that area, so all the talk about women having many orgasms at once just adds to it for me.

Sally: Right. If you experience orgasms with one person, and you don't experience them with another one, the pressure is on you to try to figure out why. It is sort of like trying to figure out what you are doing every moment. You can make the appropriate sounds at the appropriate times, but in fact you know

* The word is best avoided. It does have a proper technical application to a condition which is symptomatic of mental disorder. But in popular use it is simply a pejorative term by which men (and women) label any woman who exhibits more sexual interest than they possess themselves. Most authorities now agree that many women who have in the past been classified as nymphomaniacs were just highly sexed and in no way emotionally disturbed (Levitt, 1973).

you are acting. Then you begin to wonder, first of all, why you are acting. Secondly, you are wondering why you are not experiencing all these ecstatic feelings you had experienced before.

It is like anything else—you are supposed to measure up to the normal. What is normal for me is not normal for you. Why I am not normal like the rest of the people who are in the studies I don't know (Gadpaille, 1972).

One source of this concern is the assumption that the male pattern of orgasm should be the norm for women. Because we now know that the female is capable of orgasmic experience as intense as that of the male (Masters and Johnson, 1966), it is taken for granted that women should and can enjoy orgasm as readily and in the same circumstances as men. Because the biological identity of male and female orgasm has been established there is now an expectation that the woman will normally experience a dramatic, vigorous climax similar to the man's. Her failure to do so may be taken as a lack of sexual responsiveness or as a slight on her partner's masculinity. Some women feel it necessary to fake orgasm to impress the man.

Some men will blame a woman for being "frigid" * if she fails to perform as he expects and according to his standards of sexual pleasure. Indeed there is reason to believe that it is the male's anxiety about his own sexual capacity that leads him to demand *his* kind of sexual response from his partner (Schaefer, 1973). "If the male is secure with his own feelings about himself as a man, he need not feel threatened nor feel inadequate if his partner

* Another word best avoided. There is a very uncommon technical condition of frigidity due to physical or psychological causes and requiring therapy (McCary, 1973), but the layman wrongly uses the term indiscriminately to put down any woman who fails to respond sexually as he desires.

does not achieve orgasm. An important side effect of the female's lack of orgasm may be the development of secondary impotence or premature ejaculation on the part of the male. This may come about from the anxiety generated by his 'need to perform,' his fear of failure to bring his partner to orgasm, and by the memory of previous unsuccessful achievements" (Adelson et al., 1973).

Marcus (1966) argues that women have too easily allowed themselves to be persuaded to identify their sexual capacities with those of men, thus failing to achieve the real liberation they seek. He points out that in the nineteenth century women as well as men were convinced that there was a female ejaculation parallel to that during male orgasm. This shows us, he suggests, that women's idea of their own sexuality is "historically a response to what men want and demand that sexuality to be, and that in general women are content to accept whatever model of their own sexuality men offer to and demand of them. *Mutatis mutandis,* a little reflection will yield the insight that the same thing is happening today" (p. 113).

Another source of confusion about the "norm" of female sexual response arises from popular misreading of the Masters and Johnson studies. To take the results of their study of *Human Sexual Response* (1966) and use them as a standard by which to judge the experiences of college women is to submit to another statistical tyranny. It must be remembered that all but two of their sample were over twenty-one, *all were required as a condition of participation to have experienced orgasm during intercourse* and 357 out of the 382 female subjects were or had been married.* Furthermore, it is not sufficiently noted

---

* A similar misunderstanding may arise from reading *The Sensuous Woman* by "J" (1969). Despite its sexist orientation the book contains a lot of useful information. But what many readers fail to note is that the

that while Masters and Johnson identified only one sexual response pattern for men, they diagrammed three cycles for their female research population and described even this as an oversimplification of the "infinite variety" of female orgasmic experience.

Rather than expecting orgasmic satisfaction similar to that of the male, women should realize that "orgasm can be a very mild experience, almost as mild as a peaceful sigh, or it can be an extreme state of ecstasy with much thrashing about and momentary loss of awareness. It can last a few seconds or half a minute or longer. There is, in brief, no right or wrong way to have one" (*Our Bodies, Our Selves*, 1973, p. 33).

Reuben (1969) has taken it upon himself to tell women what they want sexually, even when women deny that orgasm is all that important to them. "Some women tell it that way," he admits, "but 'enjoying' sex without orgasm is about as satisfying as 'enjoying' a nice dinner without being able to swallow it" (p. 124). I do not question at all the importance of the recognition of female orgasmic capacity: virtually every woman, given the right conditions, can enjoy orgasm. An increasingly large number of women will do so in the future, and they will do so at an earlier age than their older sisters did. Failure to reach orgasm, once a certain level of arousal has been passed, is as frustrating and even physically painful for a woman as for a man. But most women take much longer than men to reach that level (Gebhard, 1966). Most women are more dependent than men on the emotional and personal circumstances for erotic arousal. And many women, despite Reuben's *obiter dictum,* report that they are sometimes

---

women cited as successful exponents of the art of the sensuous were mostly married (more than once) and in the late twenties or thirties—and some of their partners were in the forties or fifties!

sexually satisfied by hugging, petting or intercourse without orgasm (Bardwick, 1971; Sherfey, 1972; Stanley et al., 1973; Bell and Bell, 1972; Fisher, 1973).

Schaefer (1973) came to the conclusion that "the experience of orgasm, in and of itself, is *not* always an integral part of sexual contentment" (p. 18), and quotes this example among several: "I'm pleased and feel good whether I have an orgasm or not. It's all extremes. If I feel that he has tried to communicate with me and give something to me emotionally, that he's enjoying me and I'm enjoying him, then I don't care whether I have a climax or not. It's not that important. Of course, I wouldn't like to go every night without one. Then I would feel very frustrated and want something more" (p. 147).

No woman, then, need feel that she has to comply with some model of sexual behavior imposed by others. She is free to be a sexual person in accordance with whatever values and ideals she chooses to adopt. She can act in whatever way expresses her own inner convictions, without any obligation to perform or respond in a manner dictated by men or by other women. Schaefer (1973) sums up the situation thus: "The more thoughtful woman will realize that she must become her own authority in matters regarding her sexual conduct. She is obliged to create reasonable rules for herself. She must weigh every edict, liberal or conservative, and discard those that do not make sense for her life. The only alternative is to succumb mindlessly to the latest fashions in sexuality—which may be as repressive as earlier, orthodox styles of sexual abstinence, and may introduce anxieties considerably more difficult to dismiss" (p. 129).

Healthy sexuality depends on *both* sexes freeing themselves from a goal-oriented concern with achieving orgasm, and on enjoying different experiences of sexual intimacy for their own worth rather than as mere "foreplay" to coitus. Mature sexual values can only be established by the man or woman who is free of a sense of obligation to conform to some predetermined pattern of behavior. We have examined some of the forces that tend to inhibit that freedom by imposing new sexual uniformities. The idea that animal instincts are our masters, and that sexuality is determined by the genitals fails to do justice to the distinctness of man. We must be concerned with what Maslow has called "the farther reaches of human nature" rather than with the minimal satisfaction of physical needs. We must seek a postconventional morality which is neither the passive acceptance of nor the arbitrary rejection of what society has to teach us. There is no true freedom in conforming to peer group expectations or to the popular misrepresentation of the campus as a perpetual orgy. Statistical studies provide us with the raw material for responsible decision making, not with conclusions.

Having looked at our changing cultural background and at the complex factors that affect the individual's development of sexual values we can now examine three examples of such values: the traditional ideal of premarital chastity, the increasingly attractive prospect of recreational sex and the possibility of integrating sexuality and human relationships at different levels up to that of love and intercourse. These are not altogether exclusive, for many people combine elements of more than one, and many change their basic values as they gain in experience. I have already made clear that I believe the third to offer the best prospect of personal fulfillment; but I shall attempt to analyze each with some objectivity in the hope of enabling the student to develop his or her own values with greater clarity and consistency.

CHAPTER III

Sex Before Marriage

Everyone has sex before marriage. We're born with it and express it in our relationships from infancy on. But our culture places such special significance on intercourse that the question of sex before marriage focuses for many students on this particular sexual act. Whatever their personal practice may have been, about half of the adult population believe that sexual intercourse should take place only in the context of marriage, according to a 1973 Gallup poll. It is not so long ago that a professor at a major university was fired for writing in the campus paper that he saw no reason why sexual intercourse among mature students should not be condoned. The widespread furor raised by the John Birch Society's attack on sex education as a Communist plot to subvert American youth indicates how sensitive the public is to any questioning of the ideal of premarital virginity. And every political candidate, however liberal, finds that it is *de rigueur* to take an occasional knock at the consequences of "permissiveness" in our society.

Although the number of students sharing the view that abstinence before marriage is desirable is much lower than among the general population (Reiss, 1967, reported a

45

figure of 42 percent), we have seen that a third of the men and half of the women graduating from college have not in fact engaged in premarital coitus. So however old-fashioned and uptight this sexual standard may appear to many, it deserves more serious attention than it often receives in campus discussions. Unless the ideal of premarital virginity is to be rejected *merely* because it happens to be the accepted view in our culture it should be considered by anyone seriously facing the question of sexual values. And it can be defended on more than purely arbitrary grounds.

The defense of premarital virginity is, of course, closely linked to religious teaching, and there is a marked correlation between chastity and deeply held religious faith among college students (Bell and Chaskes, 1970; Jackson and Potkay, 1973; Arafat and Yorburg, 1973). However, the practice has been frequently advocated on the basis of fears and threats which (quite properly) carry little weight with most people today:

> There was a young lady named Wilde
> Who kept herself quite undefiled
> By thinking of Jesus
> And social diseases
> And the fear of having a child.

Pregnancy does still remain a matter of anxiety for students (Driscoll and Davis, 1971; Eastman, 1972) and should be for those who engage in intercourse without adequate precautions. Venereal disease should be of more concern than it is, in view of the present epidemic proportions of gonorrhea.* But a mature decision to preserve

* Information about birth control and venereal disease is available in the Appendix, pp. 187–219.

one's virginity cannot be based on such dangers alone, especially when we know they can be avoided with modern knowledge. Even the most devout can no longer pretend that there is a divinely ordained correlation between pre-marital intercourse and pregnancy or disease. But the argument for virginity can be presented on much more convincing grounds, and it is worth remembering that an idea may be true even if it has been accepted on false premises, or simply in subservience to authority.

To remain a virgin simply because your parents did, because they expect it of you and you haven't the independence to act differently, or because you have a lingering fear of hell-fire based on a religious dogma you no longer accept, is surely inadequate for a responsible or mature person. It may, however, be unavoidable and even wise until you are able to work out your own sexual ethic. As Kinsey (1948) pointed out, "For a person who believes that pre-marital intercourse is morally wrong there may be, as the specific histories show, conflicts which can do damage not only to marital adjustments, but to the entire personality of the individual" (p. 561). Lower (1973), while emphasizing that feelings of guilt are less widespread than is often claimed, recognizes the dangers of ignoring such reactions. The result may be unwanted and unwise early marriage undertaken because of guilt-feelings or diminished self-respect, and serious difficulty in achieving free sexual expression in marriage later on. But to incorporate the insights of religion into one's own ethical values is another matter. To find in religion the moral and emotional resources to discipline one's sexual desires in the service of God is not necessarily a sign of immaturity. The fact that an ideal has been accepted in childhood and adolescence on very inadequate grounds is no bar against its being adopted as part of a fully adult morality at college.

The Judaeo-Christian tradition teaches that marriage is a divinely ordained union of one man and one woman which makes them "one flesh" (Mark 10:7,8). Its primary purpose is the procreation of children, its secondary value the "mutual comfort" of the couple. Engaging in intercourse outside the context of marriage, without a public commitment to permanent life together, is a misuse of God-given powers and responsibilities. It is not (even in Catholic thought) necessary that every act of intercourse be directed towards conception, but the act is only justified within the context of a relationship which can, if necessary, provide the resources for the nurture and education of a child. When an unmarried couple engage in coitus the balance of sexuality is disastrously distorted, because its primary purpose and joy—as well as its challenge and cost—is negated: there does not exist between these two people the bond which would make their bodily union and pleasure appropriate. Pope Pius XI expressed the orthodox position thus: "Since the duty entrusted to parents for the good of their children is of such high dignity and of such great importance, every use of the faculty given by God for the procreation of new life is the right and privilege of the married state alone, by the law of God and of nature, and must be confined absolutely within the sacred limits of that state" (*Casti Connubii*, 1930).

Contemporary religious teachers of all faiths tend, however, to modify the emphasis on parenthood and to give at least equal stress to the value of marriage as an expression of mutual love and a source of personal fulfillment. In order to sustain marriage as an experience of deepening commitment and union, it is argued, the special unitive quality of sexual intercourse should be preserved for this relationship alone. As the promiscuous Ellen tells her daughter Jo in *A Taste of Honey*, "You always remember the first time." So Otto Piper (1960) has argued that the first experience of coitus involves a critical discovery of the self and of the other—of the essence of masculinity and femininity—which should be shared only with the person with whom one is to share one's life.* "The sexual act leads to a new and deepened understanding of oneself which is characterized by three features: it is an intuitive knowledge given in and with the sexual experience; it discloses what was thus far hidden from the individual; and its subject matter is one's Self seen in the mutual relationship in which it stands with the partner's Self" (p. 35).

In this view, therefore, to engage in coitus with anyone other than the person you marry is to exclude the privilege of sharing together in a unique experience. Hamilton (1956) has put the point effectively:

If it is true that sexual intercourse mediates a unique kind of personal knowledge, it is clear that a very special status must be given to the first experience of the sexual act. While, in a marriage, new things are always being learned about the other by a couple truly in love, it is also true that a decisive importance must be attached to the first time this mutual and intimate knowledge was ever shared. . . . The first sexual experience is so overwhelming and so different from any other experience that it is better reserved as a means of symbolizing and giving meaning to marriage (pp. 60–61).

* The argument thus becomes, strictly, one in support of intercourse only with the person you eventually marry, not in support of intercourse only after the wedding ceremony. In medieval Catholic practice a couple who engaged in intercourse were not severely condemned if they married soon after. In Puritan England and America the fact that a bride was pregnant was no particular reason for embarrassment and was sometimes recorded in the parish register. Later church attitudes became more rigid, but some contemporary Catholic authors argue that "preceremonial intercourse" is not to be regarded as the equivalent of premarital intercourse (Dedek, 1971).

Another approach, based on the ideas of Saint Paul, has been presented by Bailey. He suggests that, man being a unity of body and spirit, sexual intercourse is "a personal encounter between man and woman in which each does something to the other for good or for ill, which can never be obliterated." When a couple have coitus together (other than in cases of rape or the seduction of the young or feebleminded), he believes that they truly become "one flesh," whether they realize it or not. However much their future actions may deny it, this union, or *henosis,* remains a profoundly significant reality which affects their very being. If they are married, it provides the basis for ever-deepening community between them. If they are not, "they merely enact a hollow, ephemeral, diabolical parody of marriage which works disintegration in the personality and leaves behind a deeply-seated sense of frustration and dissatisfaction—though this may never be brought to the surface of consciousness and realized" (Bailey, 1952, pp. 53–54).

These rather metaphysical arguments may not carry much weight, but others may be more relevant and persuasive. It can be argued that since intercourse is the supreme experience of intimacy between two people it should be the expression of the supreme and permanent commitment represented by marriage. In marriage two people celebrate the development of their mutual trust, concern, care and confidence to the point at which they are ready to share all the responsibilities of life and parenthood. The public declaration of this commitment is itself a decisive act of love, and their relationship enters a new phase. Before marriage, even in the most sincere and honest engagement, neither is fully and objectively responsible for the other: after it they are legally, socially and personally committed. They are no longer independent centers of action but "one flesh," sharing all their possessions and potentialities, all their trials and tribulations. Should not the ultimate intimacy of the body be the expression of this ultimate commitment of the person? "Coition is not just genital commingling with one endocrine system calling out to another. Coition is expressive of the person, and to be authentic and not a lie it must correspond to the existing relationship of the person. . . . its authentic actuation demands that it be expressive of a love that is total self-donation, that is to say, a final, permanent and exclusive commitment" (Dedek, 1972, p. 50).

A Jewish scholar makes the same point: "Love is love precisely because it is a sharing of self, a giving of all that one is, a receiving without asking. It is a continuing openness, on the most intimate, individual level of lover to beloved. Two persons share their hopes, their fears, their wounds, their triumphs, and are thereby enriched. Should they not share their sexuality with one another? Should they not embrace each other in a physical unity as real as the one they have known as persons? For them the act of intercourse is appropriate. Yet, as the most personal and potentially the most creative of all human acts, intercourse should be limited to those with whom one is personally on a most intimate level. The ultimate intersexual expression demands a context of ultimate interpersonal concern" (Borowitz, 1969, pp. 17–18).

Other religious writers suggest that marriage is more likely to be solid and lasting if it is marked by an exclusive sharing of the supreme pleasure of sex. Suspicion, resentment and insecurity can seriously threaten marital relations, they argue, if one of the partners has enjoyed intercourse with another person. "Sexuality by its very nature," say two contemporary Catholic moralists, "demands a certain exclusiveness, possessiveness and permanence. . . .

Fidelity and the unquestioned trust of each spouse in the other's commitment to be faithful are necessary conditions of a happy marriage" (O'Neil and Donovan, 1968, pp. 130, 132). And Bertocci (1967), a Catholic layman and philosopher who has perhaps written the best defense of the traditional position, asks how those who are accustomed to intercourse before marriage expect to avoid extramarital involvements: "On what grounds does he expect to make an untroubled shift from sex-as-fun to sex as a means of expressing love in marriage? Does he expect the particular habits of emotional and bodily response which now regulate his sexual responsiveness to be easily transformed and to harmonize with the emotional and physical habits and expectations of his partner-in-love?" (pp. 151–52).

These arguments can, for some, be the basis of a coherent and healthy sexuality which includes the preservation of virginity until marriage. Those who are sincerely convinced that intercourse should be an expression of a relationship involving total lifelong commitment cannot be faulted for inconsistency or immaturity on that ground alone. Even Albert Ellis, who has a compulsive need to ridicule all traditional morality, admits as much. In a discussion in which he characterizes the association of sex with love and marriage as "Puritan bosh," he concedes: "It is character building to learn to defer pleasure for the *right* reasons—that is, for future gain. Long-range rather than short-range hedonism is a wise human goal. . . . You give up all kinds of sex satisfactions to build a relationship. Husbands and wives do this. They don't always have sex at exactly the time they want it because they frequently consider the desires of their partner. This aids their love feelings and consequently favors their enlightened self-interest" (Liswood and Ellis, 1971). To delay the joy of intercourse in order that it may be a more creative contribution to marital happiness may therefore not be (in Ellis's phrase quoted earlier) "arrant masochism" but a rational, mature and beneficial decision.

*   *   *

While premarital virginity can therefore be seriously defended, and no one need apologize for adopting this sexual value, there are three questions that it raises. First, *is the concern with virginity based in fact on a balancing of present and future goods or does it hide a feeling that sex is really something evil that should be avoided?* Unfortunately, religion has been responsible for much that is unhealthy, infantile and repressive in sexual ideas and behavior. In an earlier book, *Living With Sex* (1966), I argued that much of the distortion is absent from the Old Testament, from the life and teaching of Jesus and even from the much-maligned Saint Paul. But throughout most of the history of Christianity* sexuality has been regarded not merely as something to be controlled in order that it may be more fully enjoyed in marriage, but as something to be denied, spurned and, if possible, eliminated.

Saint Augustine, whose personal experience and brilliant mind were responsible for much of the Church's fear of sex and women, taught that all sexual pleasure was sinful—even when enjoyed in marriage and in the course of reproductive activity (though the sacrament of marriage

* Judaism, although never falling into the excesses of Christian antisexualism has, in its Orthodox form, contributed to the distortion. The *Code of Jewish Law* requires elevated religious thoughts during coitus and strict adherence to the "male superior" position; it forbids even looking at one's wife's genitals, intercourse for personal desire rather than marital duty, masturbation, dancing with a woman, hearing her sing or gazing at her hair. Frequent emissions, according to this ancient authority, result in physical decay and early death: "Great physicians said that one out of a thousand dies from other diseases, while nine hundred and ninety-nine die from sexual indulgence" (Ganzfield, 1961, p. 17).

ensured its forgiveness provided that the Christian did not positively desire the pleasure). "It is characteristic of a good Christian," he wrote, "to love in a woman the creature of God whom he desires to be transformed and renewed, but to hate corruptible and mortal intimacy and sexual intercourse—that is—to love the human being in her, but to hate what belongs to her as a wife" (Maxey, 1972, p. 212). The medieval elevation of permanent chastity as a good in itself and a requirement for the priesthood (as distinct from a special vocation) was a significant indication of the devaluation of sexuality.

When it is said of someone today that he is "living in sin" the fact that we know without asking that sexual misbehavior is meant indicates how deeply this attitude has permeated our whole culture. "Perhaps the bitterest commentary on the way in which Christian doctrine has been taught in the last few centuries," wrote Dorothy Sayers (1943), "is the fact that to the majority of people the word 'immorality' has come to mean one thing and one thing only. . . . A man may be greedy and selfish; spiteful, cruel, jealous and unjust; violent and brutal; grasping, unscrupulous and a liar; stubborn and arrogant; stupid, morose and dead to every noble instinct—and still we are ready to say of him that he is not an immoral man" (p. 3).

The consequences of religious teaching for sexual distortion and personal tragedy were well expressed in a letter to *Commonweal* (June, 1973): "I was taught that heterosexual sex was for procreation, not pleasure (even in marriage), that sexual thoughts and behavior was lustful and a mortal sin. . . . I have discussed this subject of sex with countless married Catholic women, and the guilt feelings these teachings have engendered in our women is horrifying to contemplate. Our feelings of guilt toward sex is so deep and ingrained, that we can't even enjoy sex in marriage." All too often when people talk about the importance of virginity it is not simply the preservation of sexual intercourse for a marriage partner that is involved—it is a fundamental attitude of repudiation, a total failure to come to terms with the fact of sexuality, a religiously inspired guilt that warps the whole person, a failure to acknowledge the body and its needs that can affect all our relationships.

The result has been the widespread problem of what have been called "ecclesiogenic neuroses" (Kroger, 1969). Masters and Johnson (1970) reported that the influence of "channel-visioned religious orthodoxy" on adolescents is a major cause of sexual inadequacy and dysfunction in marriage, and the most difficult factor to treat. Moreover, they concluded that "the fact that most men and women survive the handicap of strict religious orthodoxy to function with some semblance of sexual effectiveness does not mean that these men and women are truly equipped to enjoy the uninhibited freedom of sexual exchange" (p. 179). Pain in intercourse, premature ejaculation and impotence are often traceable to an anti-sexual religious upbringing. An anxious concern to preserve virginity at any cost may be symptomatic not of responsible, mature values but of a hidden and distorted refusal to accept and enjoy sexuality. Prudence Tunnadine (1967), a psychiatrist writing as a Christian, has warned that a refusal to engage in intercourse may be symptomatic of sexual immaturity which may militate against the chances of success in marriage: "Many who fear intercourse, or who cannot respond emotionally, hide their fears behind rationalizations of morality. They unconsciously take into themselves parental or religious prohibitions which are in conflict with their sexual desires which are ridden with anxiety or guilt. The marriage ceremony does not, alas, alter this unconscious conflict. To imply that a girl who waits for marriage to unite with the man she loves is less than normal would be an unfair generality. Nevertheless, in our experience, those who do commit themselves fully in love before marriage give us less anxiety about their capacity to achieve mutual response in marriage than those who do not."

A second question to be faced is: *is technical virginity more moral?* Much of the conflict suffered by students arises from the tension between religious ideals and the dynamics of sexuality. The cultural contradiction of sexual stimulation on the one hand and sexual prohibition on the other, to which attention was drawn in the first chapter, is particularly acute for the person with religious convictions about the value of virginity. Parents and churches often encourage teenagers in the early stages of sexual encounter and arousal, but then demand that an absolute line be drawn at intercourse (or somewhere short of that).* The fact is that religion has never come to terms with the reality of romantic love, a concept which it originally took (perhaps rightly) as a threat, but eventually accepted as a desirable prerequisite to marriage. Thus, when a priest or minister asks a couple why they want to be married, or whether they are "in love," he does not expect to be told that they are primarily interested in propagating the race or looking after each other in their old age. But if young people are encouraged to be "in love" it is inevitable that they will be involved in physical sexual contact which cannot be neatly restricted to holding hands or kissing.

Ecclesiastics have attempted to mimic King Canute and have optimistically assumed that the natural progression through necking and petting to intercourse can be arrested

---

* I sometimes suspect that when the minister, at the conclusion of a wedding, tells the couple that they may engage in the "liturgical kiss" he secretly hopes that this may be the first time they've gone that far!

at an arbitrary boundary by verbal injuction. A Catholic student of mine was instructed that, while kissing "in order to experience the general 'good feeling' produced by the excitement over the act" was acceptable, any kissing which resulted in "reaction in the organs of generation" was illicit and dangerous. A Protestant marriage handbook instructs male readers this way: "Before marriage it is best to keep every sort of sexual excitement toward your fiancée under complete control since it is not good for her" (Bovet, 1958, p. 52). An Orthodox Jewish guide for youth teaches that "*every and any* act of physical contact between the sexes, including holding hands, must be avoided before marriage" (Stolper, 1967, pp. 27, 35–38).

But most college students, including the devout, find that such Alice-in-Wonderland advice is irrelevant. Petting leads to sexual arousal which, past a certain point, leads to frustration or discomfort for both men and women if it is not relieved in orgasm. Some are satisfied with solitary masturbation after a date. But many eventually find that petting to orgasm is a necessary and viable alternative to intercourse. The increase in petting to orgasm as a means of sexual release which at the same time maintains a technical virginity was the major change in sexual behavior between 1920 and 1960 (Ehrmann, 1959; Reiss, 1960), and it continues to be a preferred practice for many students today (Davis, 1971; Robinson et al., 1972). As one female student put it: "Girls keep telling me that what I am isn't really virginity anymore. You know that line— what's a hymen anyway, when you've done everything else in the book? But 'that' really is the big step. That's it. . . . Petting is different. You can have all the warmth and affection and your virginity too" (Greene, 1964, p. 125).

Petting to orgasm can indeed be a means of relieving sexual tension and expressing intimacy, love and mutual concern without the guilt feelings surrounding intercourse. It can enable a couple to learn how to give each other pleasure and to enjoy their bodies in a personal context without the urgent need to "go all the way." It can preserve a significant relationship in which one or both of the partners has serious doubts about premarital intercourse, or inhibiting fears of pregnancy.

Kinsey (1948, 1953) found that petting to orgasm had positive value in preparing for orgasmic fulfillment in later intercourse. Reevy (1972) found a slight *negative* correlation between petting and marital success, but he noted that "there is no proof that absence of petting (or minimal petting) *causes* marital success." Moreover his figures were obtained in the nineteen-fifties when the cultural objections to petting were much stronger. As he recognizes, where petting takes place in a context of love or affection rather than of disgust or anxiety it is much more likely to have positive consequences.

But the question remains: *is it all that morally different from intercourse?* The student quoted above regarded herself as a virgin because she avoided intercourse, but she admitted, "I love to make love and if I like a boy, I do. Everything but—anything but—whatever you call it" (Greene, 1964, p. 125). She seems in fact to have been a promiscuous virgin—preserving a technical "purity" to satisfy her own inner sexual guilt but engaging in frequent casual intimacies with a minimum of affection or commitment. Would she have been *less* moral if she had gone all the way with one man with whom she had a deep relationship of affection or love? Might she have been better able to develop such a relationship if she had felt free to engage in intercourse? Only each individual can judge for herself or himself. But those who pride themselves on preserving virginity while engaging in casual petting are surely fooling themselves. They may do themselves more harm by indulging in irresponsible non-coital sex play than they would by coitus as a part of a serious relationship. As Gael Greene put it: "Technical virginity . . . may not carry the official onus of nonvirginal promiscuity, but it has a similar potential for ugliness and scarring . . . it can set off fierce self-recrimination, disgust, maiming loss of self-esteem" (ibid., p. 120).

Our fixation on the myth of the unbroken hymen* seems to get in the way of a balanced understanding of sexuality. Reiss (1970) reports that many Scandinavians view American women as *more* promiscuous than Swedish women because "they feel that the American female defines 'sex' too much in terms of just coitus and therefore pets intimately with many boys while remaining virginal," whereas the Swedish woman is more discriminate about petting, even though when she is affectionately involved she is more likely to have coitus (p. 46). Yet Reiss (1967) found that American adults (as distinct from students) were much more willing to approve petting when affection was lacking than to approve coitus when affection was present. In other words, the mere physical act is more significant in our culture than the personal relationships of the couple involved. One of the best recent discussions of sexuality from a religious point of view makes this pertinent point: "In our time, a pattern of many intense but short-lived relationships may be a more ominous portent of unfaithfulness than the simple failure to come virginal to the marriage relationship. In fact, our culture could unwittingly

* A myth because the hymen never entirely covers the vaginal entry and in some females it is virtually non-existent from birth. It is often stretched in regular athletic activity, during masturbation or petting, or through the use of tampons during menstruation. In a small number of cases an unusually tough hymen makes intercourse impossible until a minor surgical operation has been performed.

erode the capacity for faithfulness in its young by disregarding the emotional and spiritual significance of various forms of sexual behavior, while simplistically maintaining the arbitrary standards of technical virginity" (*Sexuality and the Human Community*, 1970, p. 28).

One final question should be asked: *does the association of intercourse and marriage help in fact to make better, more lasting, happier marriages?* One of the results of linking the two is that many couples in their teens or early twenties get married because they can't wait any longer to enjoy intercourse together, or because they have slept together and conceived a baby. And it is notorious that such early marriages result in a much higher divorce rate. Would it not be better to postpone marriage until economic or educational circumstances make it viable, and to accept intercourse earlier? Moreover, unwanted pregnancies (at least among college students) are much more likely to occur if a couple are struggling to avoid intercourse than if they have accepted it. Babies are often conceived because the parents, not wanting to admit their desire or accept responsibility for their actions, failed "on principle" to take adequate precautions and were carried away by passion. It is not the promiscuous who get caught, but the idealists who discover (too late) that they were not able to control their sexual needs and then find their marriage starting out with the heavy burden of an unwanted child.

Many people with religious scruples fear that to give in to physical desire will be disruptive of their relationships. As we have seen, this may be the case if guilt or fear about sexuality is not honestly faced and resolved. But, as the following account illustrates, this is by no means always the case:

We had held strongly all during our courtship to what we regarded as a Christian pattern of sexual conduct, that is, avoidance of premarital intercourse. We had been going together for over a year and were wanting to get married. I was eighteen and my fiancée the same age. My parents were opposed to our marriage, and we were just "spinning our wheels". . . . It was at this point that we went into intercourse. As I look back at it—it was about a year ago that this happened—I think I can see several reasons for what we did. We were so frustrated and blocked that intercourse did two things for us. First, we needed to be close to each other, and this was the way we could get the closeness we wanted. Second, it helped me feel that in spite of the objection of my parents, we were moving toward marriage. Actually, in a certain Christian sense, we were already married after intercourse. Then, perhaps there was an element of spite against our parents in what we did. It is all very complex (Kirkendall, 1961, pp. 166–67).

Many people who reject the rule of virginity do so in the interests of marriage, not because they want to destroy or downgrade it. There are those, of course, who regard all public or permanent bonds as inconsistent with personal freedom, who believe that sexual pleasure should be enjoyed for its own sake whenever the opportunity occurs. We shall discuss this point of view in the next chapter. But premarital intercourse is not the same thing as "free love" or promiscuity. Many people reject the idea of "recreational sex" and yet believe that it is best for a couple and for the good of their future marriage for them to engage in premarital coitus. One young mother stated that as a result of intercourse during their engagement she and her husband found that: "By the end of our courtship, sex was a secondary consideration in our decision to marry. We weren't looking eagerly toward marriage so we could experience the 'ultimate in human response.' We knew sex as an expression of ourselves—sometimes gentle and sweet, sometimes painful and cruel, sometimes a passionate orgy, sometimes a retreat from reality, but always a new experience. . . . We would have enough adjusting to do as man and wife—at least we would be spared the sometimes frightening and harsh experience of exploring untapped sexual responses" (Milas, 1967).

There is a danger that an engaged couple may so concentrate their energies on *avoiding* intercourse that they never have the opportunity to see each other as non-sexual objects. Concentration of hope and expectation on the blissful pleasure to be enjoyed in the distant future may distract their attention from more mundane factors which affect the desirability of the partner as a lifelong mate. The postponement of intercourse can so intensify idealistic dreams of consummate satisfaction on the wedding night that other vital aspects of the relationship are ignored. As a result a couple may find themselves virtual strangers on the honeymoon. Indeed I would argue that it is better to live together than merely to sleep together. In the latter circumstances, too, attention is easily focused on the sexual interludes to the exclusion of concern about mutual compatibility in other areas, and successful performance in bed can be mistakenly taken to imply adequate capacities as husband or wife. Premarital intercourse is more likely to be a positive contribution to mutual adjustment if it is part of a total experience of life together, rather than an occasional fleeting sexual coupling.

In the final analysis everything depends on the capacities and attitudes of the couple involved, and nobody can take refuge behind statistics or external authorities. Some will benefit from premarital intercourse; others will suffer. The issues are so complex and so dependent on individual circumstances that there is no simple answer to the question "Does premarital intercourse make for happy marriage?" * Kirkendall (1974) mentions these factors as of

---

* Despite frequent assertions to the contrary there is no statistical evi-

major importance: the capacity to build a mutually satisfying relationship and to communicate freely and honestly, the kind of teaching each of the partners has received about sexuality, their level of personal maturity and stability and the degree of mutual concern and affection they have for each other. If premarital intercourse is contrary to deeply held convictions or to traditional taboos that have not been faced and resolved, or if it conflicts with rational beliefs about the value of waiting until marriage, it may lead to the breakdown of relationships even between engaged couples or to difficulties in sexual adjustments in marriage. But now that women are free of the fear of pregnancy and better able to accept their own sexuality, they are much more likely to enjoy intercourse and much less likely to have feelings of guilt (Christensen and Gregg, 1970; Bell and Chaskes, 1970). As a result premarital intercourse is far less likely to be harmful to marital adjustment. For those who are able to accept it as a natural expression of love and commitment, without external pressure or internal anxiety, participation in the ultimate intimacy of sex before marriage may be of positive value as a preparation for the ultimate personal commitment of marriage.

---

dence to show that premarital intercourse is always a contribution to marital success. After surveying the literature Bell (1966) came to the conclusion that "in general, premarital chastity may be favorable to overall adjustment in marriage, but premarital coitus appears favorable to sexual adjustment in marriage. However, the interpretation of these two levels of adjustment must be made with care because factors that make for good sexual adjustment may have little to do with overall marital adjustment" (pp. 144–45).

CHAPTER **IV**

Recreational Sex

A famous *Playboy* cartoon encapsulated the antithesis of the position discussed in the previous chapter. It pictured a couple in bed together engaged in strenuous activity, while the man asks, "Why talk about love at a time like this?" According to this scheme of values sexual release and pleasure are an end in themselves. There is no necessary relationship between physical satisfaction and personal affection or love. There is absolutely no reason why immediate sensual enjoyment should be denied in the interests of some long-range goal. The preservation of virginity is at best pointless and at worst harmful. Sexual experience is part of the full life, and intercourse is readily available, always satisfying and beautifully simple. Women are part of the equipment of the well-to-do male and they can be turned on and off like the stereo set. Reuben (1969), while suggesting that recreational sex is more demanding because the primary goal is pure pleasure and "often there is not the same depths of emotion available to compensate for any lapses in sexual function," tells us there is nothing wrong with "funsex." Human beings, he points out, are provided with the essential equipment (penis and vagina) and "an overwhelming compulsion to use them." There is no reason (other than ignorance) why they should not ignore the objections of society and enjoy sex "for the sheer physical and emotional exhilaration of feeling all the good feelings that come from a complete sexual experience (pp. 45–47).

Hugh Hefner acknowledges that "personal sex is preferable to impersonal sex, because it includes the greatest emotional rewards" (Hefner, 1962–65), but others affirm that sex without involvement or emotional ties can be *more* enjoyable than sex with affection. Germaine Greer (1973) tells us that "a one-night stand can be the most perfect and satisfying sexual encounter of all, as long as there is no element of fraud or trickery or rip-off in the way in which it develops." Albert Ellis (1963) once said that "sex that is engaged in without love (or even friendship) can certainly be, and in innumerable cases is, one of the most satisfying of human pursuits" (p. 30).

There is a popular belief that Freud provided a rationale for recreational sex. But in fact, while Freud believed that repression (the failure to come to terms with sexuality) has disastrous consequences, he did not identify genital satisfaction with health, or advocate unrestrained sexual intercourse as a cure for neurosis (Stafford-Clark, 1967). While Freud found that many of his patients achieved freedom from repressive patterns of behavior only when they had broken the unconscious taboo on sexual activity, he did not generalize this fact into a universal principle—as if everyone who was not neurotic would necessarily engage in coitus in adolescence. In his *Three Contributions to the Theory of Sex* (1905) he declared that in the "definite normal form" of sexual life, the achievement of pleasure reaches its highest satisfaction when the sexual impulse "enters into the service of the function of propagation" and "becomes, so to say, altruistic" under the conscious control of "the higher psychic influences" (pp. 66, 96). In other words, it is not abstinence as such that is harmful or symptomatic of neurosis, but abstinence because of unconscious repression.

If a source is sought in psychoanalysis for the repudiation of sexual restraint, it is to Freud's early disciple and later critic, Wilhelm Reich, that we must go. Reich, who was the first to coin the phrase "sexual politics," believed that society has suppressed infantile and adolescent sexuality in order to develop character structures supporting political, ideological and economic serfdom. He therefore parted company with Freud because he thought the existing cultural restraints on sexual freedom should be challenged and society radically reorganized to allow for sexual fulfillment. He advocated the positive encouragement of infantile masturbation and the provision of opportunities for sexual intercourse between adolescents in suitable housing conditions with adequate contraceptives.

Whereas for Freud the id was a primitive power needing to be integrated and directed by the ego, "for Reich the ego was evil; the id was authenticity, beauty, pleasure, freedom" (Arieti, 1972, p. 57). It is the ego, the jailer acting as agent for repressive patriarchal society, that is to be overcome if man is to be free and society healthy. Thus Reich does make statements affirming that genital fulfillment is essential to human health: "Abstinence is dangerous and absolutely harmful to health. The suppressed sexual energy expresses itself in different ways. Either a nervous disturbance appears very soon, or the adolescent begins to indulge in daydreams; these interfere seriously with his work. True, those who refuse to see the connection between sexual excitation and nervous disorders may easily say that abstinence is not harmful or that it is practicable in most cases. They only see that the adolescent does live in abstinence and conclude that, therefore, it is practicable. What they overlook is that the adolescent can do it only at the price of acquiring a neurosis and other difficulties" (Reich, 1936, pp. 104–5). "There is only one thing wrong with neurotic patients: the lack of full and repeated sexual satisfaction. . . . The severity of any kind of psychic disturbance is in direct relation to the severity of the disturbance of genitality. The prognosis depends directly on the possibility of establishing the capacity for full genital satisfaction" (Reich, 1927, pp. 73–74).

The uncomplicated, joyful affirmation of the goodness of sexuality and its physical expression reflected in the work of Reich and by his contemporary disciples is a necessary corrective to the repressive attitudes of Western culture. Sex *is* fun, and we would all be much the better if we could acknowledge the fact openly and without embarrassment. Life would be intolerably dull without the sexual element in entertainment, movies and literature. Human relationships of all kinds, including those of a formal character, are the richer for the fact that we enjoy seeing, talking to and making physical contact with members of the other sex. If everyone from the President of the United States to the President of the University could learn to acknowledge the fact that we all enjoy seeing beautiful bodies in the nude there would be much less sniggering prurience and probably less sexual deviation. We need to achieve what Marcuse (1955) has called "the desublimation of reason" and to affirm the goodness of the body and of play over against the supposed "higher values" of economic productivity. Reich's premise that "the core of happiness is sexual happiness" must be taken seriously, and we must acknowledge the joy of sex as a natural, open, healthy gift which men and women can accept without embarrassment. The call to "make love, not war" is a much needed reversal of priorities; and it is characteristic that the establishment has now sought to reassert its rights in a poster that reads, "A country needs love too—see your nearest Army recruiting office."

Happily such a change is taking place even in religious circles, where the ideal of a strictly rational control of man's sexual desires has been most deeply imbedded. The difference may be illustrated by contrasting two Christian thinkers. Saint Thomas Aquinas in the thirteenth century argued that wedlock without carnal intercourse was more holy, and he and other medieval schoolmen echoed the saying of the philosopher Xystus: "He who loves his own wife too ardently is an adulterer" (Bailey, 1959, pp. 136–37). Aquinas quoted Saint Augustine to the effect that "nothing so casts down the manly mind from its heights as the fondling of women, and those bodily contacts which belong to the married state" (Maxey, 1972, p. 217). In contrast a contemporary Christian, representative of a new religious appreciation of the secular and the human, writes: "To put it plainly, for a man in his wife's arms to be hankering after the other world is, in mild terms, a piece of bad taste and not God's will. We ought to find and love God in what he actually gives us; if it pleases him to allow us to enjoy some overwhelming earthly happiness, we mustn't try to be more pious than God himself" (Bonhoeffer, 1953, p. 168).

So far, so good. But Reich is frequently assumed to have established much more than the goodness of sex and the need for a radical critique of our cultural repressions. He is claimed as the apostle of recreational sex, proclaiming the view that personal happiness is served by purely physical sexual encounters. He is honored in the campus culture as a hero of the Age of Aquarius, of a new innocence in which the body can be satisfied without the complications of sexual exclusiveness, personal involvement, guilt or jealousy. He is quoted against those who feel that sex should be something more than the rubbing of membrane against membrane. He supposedly serves to shame or embarrass the man or woman who maintains that marriage, or love or even affection are necessary conditions for intercourse.*

But this seems to me a totally unwarranted conclusion. Despite Reich's promotion of the orgasm as a key to the resolution of social and individual needs, it was never mere physical release isolated from personal relationships (except in masturbation) that he advocated. Genital freedom for him did not mean recreational sex. On the contrary, it led to the *abandonment* of sexual activity of a non-involved type. "Patients who up to the attainment of orgastic potency had no conflicts about going to prostitutes, now felt incapable of doing so. . . . Some of my female patients, married and unmarried, had been in the habit, up to time of cure, of going to bed with every Tom, Dick and Harry. Orgasmotherapy made it impossible for them to continue such behavior . . . they became 'moral,' in the sense of wanting only one partner, but one who loved and satisfied them" (Reich, 1927, pp. 151–52). Obviously this did not mean the reinstitution of any external code of premarital virginity; rather, Reich believed, an internal "sex-economic self-regulation" would operate (once the repression of external moral regulation had been cast off) to help the healthy individual integrate physical sexuality and human concern. "What I have in mind in speaking of

* Herbert Marcuse and Norman O. Brown are frequently interpreted in the same light. But Marcuse regards some sexual order as essential and regards uninhibited sexuality as a symptom of mania (see pp. 175–177) and Brown (pp. 105–107) propounds a "polymorphous sexuality" which is totally at odds with those who regard intercourse and orgasm as the be-all and end-all of sexual fulfillment.

sexuality is not neurotic mechanical coition but the loving embrace; not the urinating-into-the-woman, but making her happy" (ibid., p. 162).

In an article in *The Village Voice* (February 1, 1973), "The Counter-culture Co-opts Wilhelm Reich," Jerome Greenfield points out how misguided is the attempt to claim Reich as authority for recreational sex. "What often goes for freedom and uninhibitedness in the counter-culture—indiscriminate mating, orgies, sexual irresponsibility, interest in pornography, bisexual practices, having sex under the influence of drugs—is, from a Reichian point of view, nothing more than desperate attempts to achieve complete gratification against the obstruction of the armor, a condition that is the direct opposite of orgastic potency, that is orgastic impotence." Reich's motto, printed on the title page of the English translations of his works, was "Love, work and knowledge are the well-springs of our life. They should also govern it." Far from regarding the ability to engage in casual sex as a sign of maturity Reich taught that those who have acquired the ability for orgastic satisfaction "are far more capable of monogamous relationships than people who suffer from sexual stasis" and experience "again and again vivid sexual pleasure and gratification with the same sexual partner, [which] presupposes full sexual harmony between the sexual partners" (1936, p. 7). Sex-economy "has as its aim 'moral behavior' no less than does moral regulation . . . a complete harmony of nature and culture" based on life-affirming voluntary discipline (ibid., pp. 24–25). Promiscuity, for Reich, was "emotionally debased and sex-economically worthless." He repudiated "the temporary sexual relationship, the extreme of which is the one-hour or one-night relationship," and rejected as immature "the lascivious desire for new sexual stimuli that we see in the neurotic polygamy of adult men of the world" (ibid., pp. 119–20). He believed that those who are incapable of establishing a lasting relationship are "dominated by an infantile fixation of their love relationships, in other words, suffer from a sexual disorder" (ibid., p. 120).

The interesting thing is that despite the obvious attractions of recreational sex and the popular image of the campus as a perpetual orgy, despite the virtual breakdown of adult restrictions on sexual activity and the widespread repudiation of the ideal of virginity, there is no indication that students generally approve or practice the hedonistic philosophy of funsex. Kirkendall (1961) found that only a small percentage of men who had engaged in premarital intercourse were satisfied with purely physical satisfaction. Gael Greene (1964) found that "cold fucking" was entirely unacceptable to the women students she interviewed. Reiss (1967) reported that only 13 percent of male students and 2 percent of female students approved of coitus without affection—that is, outside a stable, affectionate relationship. Smigel and Seiden (1968) concluded that "permissiveness without affection, if we consider it comparable to a blanket endorsement of casual sex relations for both, is apparently on the decline—even more sharply for men than for women" (p. 12).

Luckey and Nass (1969) reported that a maximum (in the senior year) of 27 percent of college men and 6 percent of college women approved of coitus with someone who was only a "good friend" or a casual date, though 30 percent of the men and 7 percent of the women questioned had engaged in "one-night stands." Christensen and Gregg (1970) concluded that between 1958 and 1968 the percentage of both men and women having their first intercourse with someone other than a "steady date" or fiancé(e) had significantly *dropped,* and the number of both sexes reporting intercourse with more than one partner had also *declined*.* Davis (1971) concluded that only between 5 and 15 percent of women find intercourse acceptable on the basis of physical attraction, momentary impulse or curiosity without any particular affection, and that men tend to have experience with a girl that they love or care for rather than with a prostitute or casual pickup. Freedman and Lozoff (1972), while recording the noticeable increase in coitus among women students since 1965, assay that "thus far the majority of college women, and perhaps the majority of students, have rejected the ethic of sexual relationships in the absence of emotional commitment."

Lower (1973) found that only two out of fifty women he interviewed favored permissiveness without affection. One of the thirty women in this study who had engaged in coitus said, "For me the determining factor in premarital intercourse is the *quality* of the relationship. The relationship is far more important than anything else, no matter what it is! You must have things in common, and it is hard to separate a good relationship and a good sexual relationship. There is no division really" (p. 80). A male student commented in a discussion: "When intimacy becomes casual, and when your own personality and character and exposing yourself completely to somebody becomes casual, I think it could become very self-destructive. In fact, the more you expose a lot of yourself to a lot of people, the more you destroy yourself" (Lief and Guthrie, 1972). The objection to a one-dimensional use of sex is beautifully expressed by Benjamin in *The Graduate*. After sleeping

* The point is made with greater clarity by Christensen in his article in *Sexual Behavior* (1971). This fact is not inconsistent with the other conclusion of Christensen and Gregg that there was a liberalization of attitudes towards premarital coitus between 1958 and 1968. There was a movement away from the ideal of premarital virginity *and* away from the acceptance of sexual intimacy without personal involvement.

several times with the seductive and predatory Mrs. Robinson, he cries out against the total impersonality of their liaison: "Can't we just talk a little before doing it this time?"

These facts are once again not offered as an external criterion for determining individual sexual values: to do so would again involve introducing the tyranny of statistics. They are intended to help protect the freedom of those who might otherwise be pressured by the more vocal members of the peer group into conforming with what they perceive to be the appropriate standard on campus. The initial loneliness of homesickness, the anonymity of a large university and strong sexual needs sometimes lead freshmen into behavior they later regret. Casual sexual encounters turn out to be an innocent pastime for some. For some others they may be a necessary breakthrough into sexual liberation. But for those who associate sex with affection or love the dissociation of the physical and the emotional can have significant and painful consequences. So we must raise several questions that the exponents of recreational sex do not always face seriously.

*   *   *

First: *is sex as simple as it is made out to be?* The real inadequacy of the treatment of sex in *Playboy, Penthouse* and their lesser rivals is their superficial assumption that sex is a matter of the body and not much else. Sex is presented as a commodity, as "one of the ingredients in a total entertainment and service package for the young urban male," to quote Hugh Hefner's *Playboy Philosophy* (1962–65). Men and women are depicted as uncomplicated items to be fitted into the enjoyment of the good life as easily as a sports car or a hi-fi. Women are as physically perfect and agreeably charming as the playmate of the month—pliable, convenient and easily folded into three sections when the next attraction comes along. These influential commercial profiteers of the new liberation fall into precisely the same error as the traditional religious mores which they criticize so vigorously and so justly: they deny the contemporary psychological understanding of the depths of sexuality. The churches have wrongly treated sex as a function of the body that can be readily disciplined or dispensed with without damage to the real self. The new authorities treat it as a function of the body that can be satisfied without the involvement of the self. "Sexual love," writes Rollo May (1969), "has the power to propel human beings into situations which can destroy not only themselves but many other people at the same time. We have only to call to mind Helen and Paris, or Tristan and Iseult, which are mythic presentations, whether based on historical personages or not, of the power of sexual love to seize man and woman and lift them up into a whirlwind which defies and destroys rational control" (p. 110). If we attempt to isolate sex from the whole person we have not learned anything from Freud and his successors. We are not people who choose to act sexually, but sexual beings through and through, and to deny or to distort the interrelation of body and self is to court disaster.

We might illustrate the issue with reference to two movies. In *The Harrad Experiment,* based on Robert Rimmer's popular novel, a group of students participate in an organized study in sexual experimentation. Each is assigned a roommate of the other sex and all are free to engage in sexual intimacy as they choose. Few have any hesitation about so doing. After a series of trials and errors involving no profound or very painful experiences, differences are ironed out, the Don Juan is brought to his senses and everyone finishes up matched with an appropriate and acceptable partner. The characters are notably beautiful, cool, seldom at a loss for self-analysis, sexually efficient—and almost totally lifeless. The (true) story of a college student who tried to commit suicide because his girl friend, whom he had invited to share his room, fell in love with his roommate, would be out of place in the Harrad laboratory. The potentially destructive, frustrating and tragic consequences which are the other side of the coin of sexual openness and freedom are excluded from that aseptic atmosphere.

In contrast, Bertolucci's movie *Last Tango in Paris* portrays a chaotic, complex, distorted relationship between a man and a woman in which the implications of sexuality are deeply probed. They meet by accident in an unfurnished apartment which both of them want to rent. They couple without preliminaries and without words. They return again and again to satisfy their sexual urgencies in a variety of ways. But at the insistence of the man, Paul, they tell each other nothing of their lives outside the apartment, not even their names—though when he begins on one occasion to speak of his past she eagerly presses him to tell her more. She suffers his abuse and degradation, apparently held captive by an overpowering sexual need which her fiancé cannot meet. Eventually she declares the affair at an end, but by this time he is involved at a deeper level and can no longer keep up the charade. As he follows her into her home and cries out, "I love you—I want to know your name," she shoots him. It is a compelling story, despite its melodramatic ending, about the consequences of an uncaring relationship and the damage sex does when divorced from tenderness or human involvement. Molly Haskell, reviewing the movie in *The Village Voice* (October 26, 1972), concluded with this comment: "Is it possible to have an affair 'for sex only'? the film asks. I have asked it myself. Bertolucci finds, as I found, that the answer is NO. It is necessary. But not possible."

A second question which the proponents of funsex must take seriously is: *is it honest?* There is no doubt that the *intention* is to avoid deceiving or harming other people. Hugh Hefner (1962–65) is quite explicit in stating that he repudiates sex that is "irresponsible, exploitative, coercive, or in some way hurts one of the individuals involved." But how often does sexual enjoyment involve deception, aggression or subtle pressure which denies the other person his or her full dignity? Traditionally this kind of coercion has originated with the male. Ellis (1963), for example, offered this advice to men in a chapter called "The Art of Seduction":

Even girls who *don't* want to be talked into having sex relations with a male can frequently be persuaded, for most girls have exceptionally poor reasons for not indulging, and these reasons can often be logically undermined. . . . One of the best persuasive methods for getting a girl to go further than she originally intends is to convince her that you are not necessarily asking that she have actual intercourse with you, but you are largely trying to induce her to have some form of mutually satisfying relations that will result in orgasm for both of you. . . . On the whole, even from the very first night you make any passes at your girlfriend—which may well be the first time you meet her—you should try to go as far as you can possibly go with her sexually: since, much to your surprise, you may even be able to go all the way right at the start; and usually the further you get with her this time, the further you are likely to get with her the next time.

The number of women who are taken in, or unwillingly pressured, by such tactics is decreasing steadily. But it is still far from uncommon for a woman who has agreed to (and enjoyed) petting to find herself virtually forced into coitus by the urgency of male demand (Kanin, 1970). One out of every four males admits to having made aggressive attempts at coitus contrary to the wishes of his partner (Kanin, 1969), and one out of every four women still feels that her first experience of intercourse was due to force or to a sense of imposed obligation (Christensen, 1971).* In an article called "The Civilized Rapist" (*The Village Voice,* September 9, 1971), an anonymous author quotes the secret of Sanche de Gramont: "I discovered magic words that uncrossed legs, and magic potions and talismans. It never occurred to me to use force. The normal currency of courtship provided. A man with money in his pocket to buy food doesn't steal it. Courtship and rape pursue a similar end, the first in a voluntary and reciprocal manner, the second at knife-point."

Germaine Greer (1973) describes the effects of what she calls "petty rape." "Rape by fraud—by phony tenderness or false promises of an enduring relationship," she writes, "corrodes a woman's self-esteem so that she grows by degrees not to care too much what happens or how. In her low moments she calls all men bastards; she enters into new relationships with suspicion and a forlorn hope that maybe this time she will get a fair deal. . . . The results of this hardening of the heart are eventually much worse than the consequences of fortuitous sexual assault by a stranger, the more so because they are internalized, insidious and imperceptible."

Of course many men who deceive a woman also deceive themselves and later come to understand with sorrow that what for them was merely recreation was something much

---

* It should be noted however that between 1958 and 1968 this figure dropped from 38 to 23 percent (Christensen, 1971).

more significant and painful for their partner. Here is one example:

I met a girl and started making love to her. Eventually she fell in love with me. (At least she thought she loved me and that, I think amounts to the same thing. In other words, she could be badly hurt.) One day we were alone in my father's home and we decided to make love. This we accomplished in a bedroom on the second floor. After we finished, she wanted to be kissed and to hear that I loved her—anything at all that would *justify the act*. What she did not know was that I *felt nothing but a physical attraction for her* and wanted no part of her after we were finished. . . . For the first time I realized the damage I had done (Kronhausen and Kronhausen, 1960, pp. 212–13).

Aggression* is, of course, far from being a male prerogative. A woman can be just as unscrupulous in using sex for purely selfish ends, though aggression in a woman is usually more subtle. It often takes the form of manipulating other people, of what Judith Bardwick (1971) calls "the tyranny of the weak." Berne (1964) describes the sport of "Rapo" in which the woman derives satisfaction from flirting with a man to the point of coitus and then rejecting him. What Hartogs and Fantel (1967) call the "compulsive castrator" is not an unknown phenomenon on the campus. Here is a description by Margaret Drabble, in her novel *The Waterfall* (1969), of a student at Cambridge University:

* I use the word *aggression* here in the popular sense of action that achieves its end at the expense of another through overt or covert violence. In another sense aggression is a necessary and constructive factor in human life, and as defined by Lorenz (1967), May (1969), Tiger (1969) or Storr (1968), it is virtually equivalent to "initiative" or "willed action" and quite distinguishable from coercion or dominance by force.

By the end of her first year Lucy was established as a *femme fatale,* of a kind familiar to that small world—not cheerful, not even casual about her affections, but emotionally promiscuous, faithlessly intense, universally sincere. People fell in love with her to suffer, to share her exploratory sufferings, to share a share of her bed. She collected them. She liked their devotions, their pain. She thrived on them, grew strong on the arousing of unrequited passion. She sat there in her room in Newnham, a pale queen, and they gathered round her, seeking destruction; tenderly she wept over them, as she pulled off their wings, tenderly she drank coffee with them, and discussed their grief.

Some forms of coercion are blatant and obvious. To say "If you loved me you'd sleep with me" is a piece of overt blackmail to which the obvious rejoinder is "If you loved me you wouldn't pressure me into behavior I don't really desire." But even to say "I love you" or "Do you love me?" when you know there is no real affection present is a dishonest play on emotions. For a man to sleep with a girl who is a virgin when he wants the girl he marries to be a virgin (as a significant number of college men still do: Luckey and Nass, 1969; Kaats and Davis, 1970; Christensen, 1971) is to put her out of the market for the kind of marriage he thinks desirable. To engage in intercourse for the fun of it when you know you have, or may have, a venereal disease is to do real or potential harm to another person. It is a form of covert aggression to run the risk of pregnancy because you can't be bothered to take the necessary precautions or won't be satisfied with petting to orgasm.

One woman described her experience with a man with whom she was having a purely physical sexual relationship, and to whom she was vulnerable because of a need for companionship. "I needed to trust somebody, so I decided to trust him. He gave me a whole big story about being found sterile on several examinations. He assured me there was no reason for me to use my diaphragm. So when he said, with tears in his eyes, that he could never be a father I believed him. Anyway, as a result I got pregnant. At first I expected him to say, 'Oh, wow, you're pregnant, that's fantastic. I didn't think I could be a father!' I was hoping and praying he did not purposely do this thing to me. But all he said was that the decision about an abortion is up to me. I realized that he got me pregnant deliberately. Then he wouldn't help finance the abortion. That is a pretty damn sick way for a person to get his masculinity" (Gould, 1971).

But it's not only men who use people sexually to bolster their own self-esteem. Women do still get pregnant because they want to catch a particular boy by involving him in the obligations of parenthood. Some who cannot accept the fact of their own sexuality fail or "forget" to use any contraceptive so that if they conceive they can blame the man or at least claim it was an accident—at his expense. Many psychiatrists think that the continued high level of unwanted pregnancies is due to the fact that some women want to become pregnant as a means of establishing their identity or independence: "Although consciously they may believe that they have no desire to have a baby, unconsciously they may harbor a strong wish to prove themselves adequate as women by producing a child" (Blaine, 1967).

Another question to be put to those who separate sex from commitment or affection is: *is it dehumanizing?* For there can be no question that recreational sex is always in danger of treating people as merely convenient objects for pleasure. In Malraux's novel *Man's Fate* the author says of one character, Ferral, "In reality he never went to bed with anyone but himself, but he could do this only if he were not alone." And we can use another person's body so as to deny their humanity even when there is no physical contact. Consider the following example:

A young woman is walking down a city street. She is excruciatingly aware of her appearance and of the reaction to it (imagined or real) of every person she meets. She walks through a group of construction workers who are eating lunch in a line along the pavement. Her stomach tightens with terror and revulsion; her face becomes contorted into a grimace of self-control and fake unawareness; her walk and carriage become stiff and dehumanized. No matter what they say to her, it will be unbearable. She knows that they will not physically assault her or hurt her. They will only do so metaphorically. What they will do is *impinge* on her. They will demand that her thoughts be focussed on them. They will use her body with their eyes. They will evaluate her market price. They will comment on her defects, or compare them to those of other passersby. They will make her a participant in their fantasies without asking if she is willing. They will make her feel ridiculous, or grotesquely sexual, or hideously ugly. Above all they will make her feel like a *thing* (Tax, 1970).

On the other hand instead of being impinged upon by impersonal and external attitudes, a person may be reduced to indignity and self-loathing by the isolation of the genitals from human relationships. Here is a description of a well-educated, intelligent and sophisticated girl who thought of herself simply as a sex machine:

The main symptoms of her difficulty were her inability to form any meaningful and lasting attachments and her tendency to make up in sheer numbers what her relationships lacked in quality. . . . Ingeborg the cunt was put at everyone's disposal so that Ingeborg the person would remain out of the reach of all outsiders. But the stratagem backfired. Ingeborg the person eventually moved out of reach of even Ingeborg herself. As her language indicated, all that remained, even in her own view, was Ingeborg the cunt (Hartogs and Fantel, 1967, pp. 123–24).

Prostitution and pornography represent two logical conclusions to funsex. In the first men get their pleasure (or, in the case of pimps, their livelihood) from the debasement of human beings to the level of mere objects. It makes no difference that women (and men) choose prostitution as a way of life because it offers (initially) economic attractions: the fact is that they are treated as a mere assemblage of tissue, muscle and flesh for someone else's purely physical satisfaction. The fact that many female prostitutes are unconsciously getting back at the male sex by obliging the customer to pay for her services, and thus humiliating him, only makes more clear the exploitative character of the business. As Winick and Kinsie (1971) put it in a classic understatement: "Prostitution is beyond doubt a social evil because it uses up women in a very rough way."

Pornography again is characterized by its concentration on the genitals to the exclusion of all other interests, and its primary appeal is to those whose psychosexual development has been arrested, so that they prefer a purely impersonal, non-demanding sexual object for stimulation, rather than a living, identifiable and possibly threatening human being.* Indeed the crucial distinction between true por-

---

* As I have already made clear, I am opposed to any form of censorship for adults. People should be allowed to read or view what they want. Erotic materials can serve a purpose, properly interpreted, in sex education; and some married couples find them helpful to boost their lagging sexual energies. But this does *not* mean that hard-core pornography is desirable or worth safeguarding for its own sake. Two members of the Commission on Obscenity and Pornography rightly described it as "vulgar, distasteful, dull, a waste of money, and rapidly boring." They were surely right in claiming that all of the commissioners felt as they did and that they repudiated censorship in the hope of diminishing interest in pornography and developing healthy and mature sexual attitudes (*Report of the Commission on Obscenity and Pornography*, 1970, pp. 453, 455).

nography and erotic literature is the total absence from the former of any development of plot or character. One viewer of *Deep Throat* commented, "It was just like watching cattle," and however superior it was in technique and photography that movie still featured sex organs totally disengaged from human beings. For this reason Marcus (1966) rightly concluded that Frank Harris's autobiographical *My Secret Life* is not totally pornographic because although the author saw Europe "through the eye of a penis" he evinced a modicum of concern for the social condition of one of his partners.

Norman Mailer (1971) has shown that Kate Millett's strictures on Henry Miller are exaggerated, but it is still difficult to avoid the conclusion that much of Miller's writing, despite its brilliance and rambunctious vigor, is basically dehumanizing. Millett (1970) writes that "with Miller the commercialization of sexuality is not only a gratifying convenience for the male (since it is easier to pay than persuade) but the perfection of feminine existence, efficiently confining it to the function of absolute cunt" (p. 301). While his wife, Maude, protests that he has no respect for her as a human being, Miller (in *Sexus*) avows his preference for "cold fuck" without any tears or "love-business" while she is half-asleep and dreaming. And he boasts (in *Tropic of Capricorn*) that the best fuck he ever had was with a half-witted woman, since "perhaps that was what made her cunt so marvelously impersonal."

Mailer (1971) pays humble tribute to just this quality in Miller's (and by implication in his own) attitude to sexuality: "One followed the line of one's sexual impulse without a backward look at what was moral, responsible or remotely desirable for society . . . one set out to feed one's cock (as man from the Renaissance had set out to feed his brain) and since the effort was pioneer in the very real way that no literary man with the power to shift consciousness had ever given that much attention before to the vagaries and outright contradictions of a stiff prick without a modicum of conscience, no one had ever dared to assume that such a life might be as happy and amusing as the next, that the paganism of a big-city fucker had its own balance, and such a man could therefore wage an all-out war to storm the mysteries with his phallus as a searchlight because all sexual experience was valid if one looked at it clearly and no fuck was in vain" (p. 77). It is difficult to know how such a position is consistent with full respect for the dignity and personhood of those who may be the objects of the Miller-Mailer machismo.

One final question: *is recreational sex healthy?* It is hard to draw the line between the type of sexual behavior we are discussing and that symptomatic of neurotic promiscuity,* and those who advocate sex without involvement appear to be offering a prescription for personal and sexual immaturity. Fromm (1956) writes that "the obvious clinical facts demonstrate that men—and women—who devote their lives to unrestricted sexual satisfaction do not attain happiness and very often suffer from severe neurotic conflicts or symptoms. The complete satisfaction of all instinctual needs is not only not a basis for happiness, it does not even guarantee sanity" (pp. 77–78). May (1966) concludes that promiscuity is a symptom of personal inadequacy: "The less mature the person, the more the simply physiological gratification itself carries the value and the

---

* It is vital to distinguish between pre- or non-marital sex and promiscuity. A failure to do so, as we have noted earlier in the case of Vance Packard's *The Sexual Wilderness* (1968), results in a very distorted picture of sexual behavior on campus. Promiscuity is "the indiscriminate compulsive seeking of a series of transient sexual encounters based neither on love nor on friendship but merely on the relief of sexual tensions, in which little or no significance is attached to the non-sexual attributes of the partners" (Willis, 1967b, p. 16).

less difference is made by *who* gives the gratification; whereas the more mature and differentiated the person, the more such other factors as tenderness and the personal relationship to the other person determine the value of the sexual experience" (p. 73).

Keniston (1965) found that alienated students typically viewed sex in purely sensual terms, found little satisfaction in it and tended to establish only superficial relationships. Halleck, on the basis of his work as Director of Student Psychiatry at the University of Wisconsin reported that "students who are psychiatric patients are likely to be promiscuous. Many of these patients, both male and female, can be described as alienated, and alienated students are especially promiscuous. While the alienated student seems to be leading a sexually stimulating life, he frequently complains that it is unsatisfying and meaningless. Intimacy, self-respect, and even orgasm are usually lacking" (*The New York Times*, May 12, 1967). Freedman and Lozoff (1972) concluded that

those college seniors who seemed the "best off" sexually—that is, those who, regardless of actual experience, seemed to have a considerable capacity for warmth, intimacy, and bodily enjoyment and at the same time an appropriate amount of control over their sexual behavior—were not likely to have been sexually precocious. Some students who had commenced sexual intercourse on a regular basis fairly early in their secondary school years did not present a favorable picture when they were seniors in college. Some of them had deep-lying personality difficulties. Some of the men were insensitive and shallow. Both men and women conveyed the impression of individuals who were not likely to travel very far along the paths of intellectual and personal development. Those seniors who seemed to be going a long way in terms of personality development had a history of rather slow and gradual unfolding of sexual interests and behavior.

Persistent sexual promiscuity is probably due to inadequate relationships in infancy and childhood. A boy who is never directly exposed to a male model of consistency and fidelity may find it difficult to develop a capacity for self-giving love and loyalty. A girl who has been betrayed by someone in whom she had placed her confidence may react later by defensively avoiding any commitment in sexual relationships. The child who is the product of a broken, disorganized or excessively conflicting home may be liable to assume that any personal bond is threatening to his own security and happiness. Students who have such problems can and should seek professional counsel.

This does not mean that an occasional experience of recreational sex is symptomatic of serious emotional immaturity. Katz (1968) found that "many freshman women engage for a period in rather 'promiscuous' dating, often to convince themselves that they are desirable even though intellectual" (p. 52). Those whose background is supportive and healthy are not likely to be significantly or permanently affected by the spurious attractions of "short-order sex." Particularly in adolescence recreational sex as a form of experimentation may have little significance (except to other individuals who may be the objects of experimentation). But the college student should graduate from this type of behavior as definitely as he or she has graduated from high school. As a continuing pattern May (1969) believes that promiscuous behavior can "set the stage for the development of impotence and affectlessness later on" (p. 105). "Sexual love . . . can not only be play, but probably an element of sheer play should be regularly present . . . casual relationships in sex may have their gratification or meaning in the sharing of pleasure and tenderness," he acknowledges. "But if one's whole pattern and attitude toward sex is only casual, then sooner or later the playing itself becomes boring. The same is true of sensuality, obviously an element in any gratifying sexual love: if it has to carry the whole weight of the relationship, it becomes cloying. If sex is only sensuality, you sooner or later turn against sex itself" (ibid., p. 313).

The values and influence of those who advocate impersonal sex as a way of life or practice it in preference to affective and integrative relationships may have long-term consequences for our society. Kirkendall (1961), elaborating on the ideal of interpersonal relationships as the criterion of sexual value, points out that "a good relationship between two or a few persons is like a stone cast in a pool of water. It creates an ever-widening circle of ripples, which eventually reach the farthest bank" (pp. 7–8). But the opposite is true also. In a *Newsweek* cover story (July 16, 1973) called "Games Singles Play," the satisfactions and pleasures of prolonged post-adolescence were recorded and the claim of many participants to have found the Good Life was acknowledged. But the article noted that the fun and gamesmanship was also "tinged with frustration, loneliness and quiet desperation." The proprietor of a singles bar described it as "a place where predatory men prey on neurotic women and where impotent men are preyed upon by castrating females." "While some score and others strike out," said the article, there is for both "a sobering degree of loneliness and *tristesse*," and the longer many "swingles" play their roles the harder they find it to "break off the quest for new conquests and the conditioned adjustment to a paucity of communication and commitment." One woman remarked, "Sex has gotten so cheap," and another said, "The whole scene begins to seem so empty, so contrived. It's simply not the kind of place to be growing up in."

This fear, that recreational sex is threatening us with a

cultural loss of the capacity for deep affection or love, was reflected in *The Village Voice* column "Scenes" (November 16, 1972). After remarking that the big question in today's sophisticated society is not "Can marriage last" or even "Can two people live together" but "Can two people get along for a week-end," the author continued with this lament:

Maybe it's some sort of sexual revolution backlash. Sex is so easy to come by; you don't *have* to form a relationship to get it, so there's no reason to even try and work something out with someone.

Another friend said it was an age thing, that only the younger people are still naive enough to believe in fidelity and true love and commitment; and another friend said it was just the other way around, that it was the kids who were adjusting better to the freedom; but all I know is that in *all* age groups people have become chary of closeness and leery of sex. Because, after all, even random sex does resemble closeness. And that's the real backlash.

Maybe it's because we're still puritan enough to expect that sex means *some* sort of commitment, and yet we don't want to take the responsibility. In any case, something's happening.

CHAPTER V

The New Sexuality

The sexual value systems discussed in the previous two chapters have been shown to be far more complex than their proponents often recognize. It is not clearly the case that waiting for marriage is the best way to strengthen marriage, or that a failure to do so is irresponsible. On the other hand recreational sex, whatever its immediate satisfactions for those capable of divorcing the emotional life from the physical, potentially involves dishonesty, dehumanization of the partner and personal immaturity. But there is one simple point on which those who advocate chastity and those who advocate funsex agree: they tend to identify sex with intercourse and orgasm. The whole range of sexual interaction, from the first shy, groping attempt at communication through the exciting exploration of another person's body, is regarded as mere "foreplay." Everything up to and including heavy petting may be acceptable to the traditionalist because it does not involve "having sex."

Recreational sex is equally indifferent to the preliminaries: it is "scoring," "getting laid," "balling" that counts. Coital orgasm is an isolated goal to which all other concerns are subordinated. Human sexual relationships are reduced to the single-minded pursuit of climactic ecstasy. "Sex, like work, becomes a matter of performance. There is always a goal in view—ejaculation for the man, orgasm for the woman. If these goals are achieved the job has been satisfactorily performed. . . . Both partners will be pleased by their sexual performance. Sex, for them, is not a way of being, a way of expressing identity or feelings or a way of nourishing a commitment. It is always a single incident, an occasion, an accomplishment. Goal-oriented sex concentrates on this moment and this act. It demands gratification now. Usually, goal-oriented sex is self-defeating. Sex interest is soon lost as the result of performance demand. At first, there may be extraordinary high sensate response, but a steady decline in sexual interest is virtually inevitable because the power to evoke sexual response by purely physical, tactile stimulation is subject to the law of diminishing return" (Masters and Johnson, 1972).

If the experience of sex on campus is to be truly maturing we have to break free of this hang-up on intercourse or orgasm as the focus of sexual achievement. We have to explore sexuality for its own worth, rather than seeking and using sex as a means to social order or individual pleasure. We have to recognize the unavoidability of sexuality* and its integral connection with emotional growth at every stage of development if we are to enjoy sexual and personal fulfillment. We have to recognize that sexuality involves the basic fabric of our lives and that the adequacy or inadequacy of our sexual self-understanding will affect both our present role as a student and our future career, social relations, family status and emotional health. To quote the

---

* A religious publishing house recently put out a volume in a series on sex education with the unbelievable title *Life Can Be Sexual*—as if it can be anything else!

British psychiatrist Anthony Storr (1964), whose writing in this field I find among the most helpful:

Sex is so important, so pervasive, and so intimately connected with every aspect of personality that it cannot be separated from the person as a whole without impoverishing even superficial relationships. There are times when we meet other human beings simply to exchange information, or to discuss ideas, or in some professional setting. On such occasions the sexual aspect of ourselves is of minimal importance. But directly we meet people socially as people, our attitude to our own sexuality and to theirs becomes significant; for the kind of contact which we make with each other in ordinary social exchanges at a superficial level is determined by the capacity we possess for making deeply intimate relationships; and the ideal sexual relationship is probably the deepest and most intimate which we can experience (pp. 9–10).

Lowen (1965) suggests that we have a great deal of sexual sophistication but little sexual maturity, and that "the current sexual sophistication is a cloak that covers and hides the sexual immaturity, conflicts and anxieties of its wearer," who is in fact "confused about his sexual role and uncertain of his sexual goals" (p. 1).

Much energetic devotion to sexual experimentation and what is euphemistically called "free love" hides a profound need for the quality of interpersonal empathy and communication that would make sexual intimacy, including coitus, meaningful and rich. The problem is beautifully expressed in a passage in that hilarious but bitter novel *Such Good Friends*.* Fantasying about her relationships with a friend, Julie imagines herself explaining the situation to an enquiring judge: "We made love, your honor.

* By Lois Gould, Dell, 1970.

He didn't have any, and neither did I. So we made some. It was good." The fact that the phrase "make love" means only one thing to us, namely intercourse, is itself a significant indicator of the problem. The fact that to "make" someone is to have intercourse with them with a suggestion of conquest is another illustration of the extent to which sex has become functional. Preoccupation with techniques is symptomatic of our age, and the tragedy of our society is that instead of technology serving people, people are in bondage to it. The ecological crisis is stark testimony to the fact.

As Kenneth Keniston (1965) concluded on the basis of his study of the "alienating society," "the deification of instrumentality" puts "the pursuit of sheer quantity and the quest for expertise" above the goal of quality and depth. And specifically in the sexual sphere the isolation of the practical and physical from the richness and integrity of the personal is illustrated, Keniston suggests, by the fact that the word "passion" is now virtually synonymous with sexual excitation, and hardly ever conveys deep or ennobling feeling or dedication to an ethical or spiritual ideal. A reviewer of John Updike's least impressive novel, *Couples,* was moved to remark that for our culture sex is merely "the ultimate in consumer goods"—a valid inference from that dreary diary of senseless and sensual coupling and uncoupling. I suggest that an earlier example of the same genre of adulterous suburban tedium, James Gould Cozzens's *By Love Possessed,* should by rights have been entitled *By Lust Possessed.*

The college student has a unique opportunity to develop a capacity for truly personal sexuality. But we have to recognize the problems many men and women bring with them to the campus. A virtual relearning of attitudes and even of facts may be necessary if the distortions of adolescence and preadolescence are to be corrected and healthy openness to sexuality established. Many men have difficulty entering into a warm, close, open relationship with others. They have been taught that to be tender and sensitive is "sissy" and, as a result, learn to restrict their emotional and physical self-expression. When the opportunity and demand of intimacy offers itself they may lack the capacity to be open and unembarrassed about their true feelings (or even the ability to acknowledge them consciously). As a result their sexual relations may be marked by rigidity and aggressiveness, and by a failure to enjoy the pleasure of sexual contact other than in intercourse—the one act which (perhaps because of the symbolism of penetration and entry) is perceived as consistent with the male machismo.

The double standard, which not only requires male demonstration of sexual prowess but also assumes that "nice girls" will not "go all the way," is in its decline, but far from dead. A satirical review, *The Committee* (*Reprise* records, No. 2023), has a man showing a woman round the fraternity house. He invites her to view the bedroom and when she demurs points out that after going together for some time, "We've come to a point in our relationship where we can share something far greater, more important, much more beautiful." She replies, "Look, Si, I can't just do it for a sharing experience. What if I did share with you, and then I found out I didn't love you. So then I met somebody else and had deep feelings for them too, and so then I shared with them. . . . And then I met somebody else and I just kept on sharing and sharing and sharing." He has to be satisfied with less than what he wants, but when his roommate asks later, "Did you score?" he replies gaily, "Of course; don't I always?"

The very words used to describe sexual conquests—lay-ing, scoring, making, screwing*—convey the atmosphere of goal-oriented achievement that renders sensitivity, responsiveness, awareness, involvement or hesitation inappropriate. Caring is too close to crying, and little boys are well indoctrinated with the fact that that's not a thing they do. I was vividly reminded of the persistence of this attitude when the seven-year-old son of a returning Vietnam POW, on meeting his father for the first time in several years, went up to him and solemnly shook his hand. We need liberation from the stereotype of the sexually dominant, uninvolved, coolly purposeful male as much as from the stereotype of the dependent, emotional, sexually uninterested female coyly using her available weapons to trap him into marriage.

But it is precisely this ethos that characterizes what Germaine Greer (1971) calls "the teasing and titillation of dating." In the socially acceptable form of adolescent sexual encounter the girl is encouraged to entice the boy to the very gate of the citadel, while being sure to deny him entrance. She must defend herself from penetration while ensuring that the attacker's interest is not diverted or his hope for conquest extinguished. The woman is encouraged to want the man to want intercourse but equally discouraged from allowing him the opportunity. "You're annoyed if a boy tries to make you on a first date because it shows he thinks you're easy," said one British teenager, "and you're annoyed if he *doesn't* try to make you because it shows he doesn't fancy you" (Hamblett and Deverson, 1964, p. 32).

---

* "Fuck" has a parallel but reverse function. Instead of taking a word from the vocabulary of aggression and applying it to the sexual act we take the word from the act and use it to enrich the language of aggression. In business, says Henry Miller, "it's fuck or be fucked." "Fuck off" or "fuck you" are clear enough in their intention.

Adolescent relationships between the sexes all too often resemble a carefully planned and cunningly executed assault on the one hand, and a more or less persistent resistance in defense of virginity on the other. The fact that nowadays the girl usually gives in eventually does not affect the fact that the *style* of male-female interaction is established on these antagonistic terms. Whether the boy reaches his objective or the girl succeeds in retaining his attentions while preserving herself inviolate, the whole operation is so centered on gaining certain goals that the wider range of personal relationships is minimized. The procedure is so ritualized in terms of an adversary relationship that each is on guard to avoid any encounter in depth. Hesitation by the boy or honest affection by the girl would undermine the only role they know. Serious conversation might reveal inadequacies. Cooperation would defuse the excitement of the chase. The family featured in the CBS documentary "What if the dream came true?" spoke for our sexual mores too when asked why they wanted to move on from one luxurious home to an even more affluent neighborhood. It's simple, they replied, "competition is the thing."

Because competition is the thing, true friendship is almost impossible to develop. "Boys, we said, were the ones who really counted. Girls were 'just friends' and therefore to be put in second place as supplements to our concern with boys. The result of that, given the nature of those early adolescent boy-girl contacts, was that friendships, particularly sexual friendships, were automatically devaluated, and sex, even if it was devoid of tenderness, devoid of an understanding we would have *demanded* from our friendships, was acclaimed the champ. The process that had been affirmed in our friendships—closeness first and sex growing out of it—was reversed. If friendship entered into our relationships with boys, it was by a freak chance. Sex brought us together. And closeness was extraneous" (Bengis, 1972, pp. 131–32).

Because competition is the thing the merchandise must be packaged to sell. The appropriate image must be projected and the real qualities of the person obscured. A thirteenth century treatise, *The Art of Courtly Love* by Andreas Capellanus, gives us a foretaste of Madison Avenue techniques applied to human relationships:

Now let us see in what ways love may be decreased. Too many opportunities for exchanging solaces, too many opportunities of seeing the loved one, too much chance to talk to each other all decrease love, and so does an uncultured appearance or manner of walking on the part of the lover or the sudden loss of his property. Love decreases, too, if the woman finds that her lover is foolish and indiscreet, or if he seems to go beyond reasonable bounds in his demands for love, or if she sees that he has no regard for her modesty and will not forgive her bashfulness. Love decreases, too, if the woman considers that her lover is cowardly in battle, or sees that he is unrestrained in his speech or spoiled by the vice of arrogance (Crosby, 1972, p. 10).*

The superficiality of this minuet of misrepresentation has fortunately been recognized by many college students.

---

* Cuber and Haroff (1966) quote a married physician who had discovered too late how such deceits cover over deep incompatibilities: "A cutie who can toss the lines with you, get you stared at at the fraternity formal, whose daddy has convinced her that if she's coy enough there'll always be a man to take care of her, can be a hell of a lot of fun while you're living out your adolescence. But *grow up* and her perpetual immaturity, her built-in inability to change from being a girly-girl, her childishness about the real world and the problems in it—why I've got another child, that's all. She needs more day-to-day wet-nursing than my twelve-year-old daughter. The girl I was so proud of and who did so many things with me in my twenties became an albatross around my aching neck" (pp. 79–80).

They have seen the tragedy of marriages based on external appearances and contrived impressions. One woman arguing for cohabitation as the more honest alternative said, "It gives you a chance to find out if there's going to be any disillusionment, and if there is, you can walk out. If you've just gone out on dates and you're on your best behavior with false eyelashes and everything, and then you get married and take off the false eyelashes, well, then you're stuck. You're in the bag, and there's nothing you can do—except divorce" (Klemensrud, 1968). But there are a great many who, while modifying the formalities of dating, remain captive to a pattern of sexual behavior that fails to break through the barrier of misunderstanding and role playing. In the ritual of advance, resistance and (usually) capitula tion increasing degrees of physical intimacy are enjoyed without any simultaneous development of personal involvement. Even the language of love is not intended or taken as an expression of serious commitment or concern; it merely forms a conventional background for sexual coupling.

One consequence of this dependence on stereotyped role playing is a failure to interpret the signals of sexual interest on each side. Because men are usually ready and eager for physical intimacy at an early stage of a relationship they tend to put the most positive interpretation on any show of sexual invitation. In a study of "The Silent Sex Game" Denfeld (1973) reported that men assumed that a woman without a bra and wearing a miniskirt was signaling that she was "permissive," "an easy ball," "available," "horny," "a loose girl" or a "sure thing." Bernard (1968) draws attention to a distinction both parties often fail to recognize: "Most men refuse to believe, or cannot believe, that the nubile young woman, luscious in her tennis shorts or bikini, is not deliberately signaling a come-on. But the signal is not necessarily the one the men pick up. She may be asking for admiration; the man hopes she is asking for him. Her body keeps signaling: I am a desirable woman. The men who see her reply, Don't be so damn provocative about it unless you want us to make something of it. The clothes, designed by knowing men, seem to signal clear and loud, Take me! The girl may actually mean nothing more than, Admire me" (pp. 83–84).

Those of us who sympathize with the concern that women be free of the obligation to compete for male attention by prettying themselves up or exposing the maximum of bare flesh may deplore this situation, but it still exists and still inhibits honest sexual relationships. Men still justify, to themselves and to their friends, overriding a woman's appeals for restraint with the confident explanation: "She asked me to stop, but I know she didn't mean it." The muffled "Please, not yet" is taken (often quite sincerely) as a mere concession to past convention; the woman is assumed to be as fired up as the man, although she feels it necessary to pretend otherwise. In the movie *The Heartbreak Kid* the following conversation takes place between the engaged Lila and Lenny in the course of a heavy petting session. "Please don't." "Why?" "I don't want you to." "Yes you do." "Can't you wait two more days?" "Nobody waits anymore." *

The naive male psychologizing behind this exchange is based on two assumptions. First, there is the sexist presumption that any girl will welcome the erotic attentions of a man—particularly the man in question. Second, there

---

* In this particular case whether Lenny persisted or not would have made no difference to the tragic outcome. They get married without any real knowledge of each other's (considerable) shortcomings, and Lenny drops her for an empty blonde beauty on the second day of the honeymoon.

is the fact that women are now known to be at least as sexually responsive as men. But what is wrongly taken for granted is that women are as ready for full sexual intimacy as early in a relationship as men. Of course some women are more interested in intercourse than some men. Whether the existing differences will prove to be entirely culturally conditioned and whether they will eventually be eliminated remains, as we shall see, an open question. But it is certainly not the case now that any man can assume without question that his partner wants to express her affection in *his* way, or that intercourse is as immediate a goal for her as it is for him. On the basis of her studies Judith Bardwick (1971) concludes that:

Adolescent girls enjoy flirting, kissing, and petting, but they are not motivated by strong, specifically genital urges. . . . The boy's sexual development is comparatively simple and linear. The extremely erotic penis, which has been perceptually dominant since earliest childhood, remains the executor of his sexuality. The girl is less invested in the genitals and genital sexuality because of the internal nature of her reproductive organs and the lesser sensitivity of those organs. A general body sensuality and a need for love are more significant for the adolescent girl than physical sexuality. . . . Her sexual feelings are more diffuse than specific although she is increasingly aware that her body is a source of pleasure and a source of (menstrual) pain (pp. 51–52).

What may be an obvious expression of the man's affection for (and need of) her may be unattractive and inappropriate to the woman. If she enjoys his company and wants to deepen the relationship she may accept further intimacies, not because she really wants them but because he does and she wants to please him. She may assume that because *for her* passionate love-making would be the expression of a deep commitment, the man's persistence and enthusiasm reflect a similar devotion. He, for his part, may wrongly suppose that her readiness for petting reflects serious erotic arousal (as it would in him), and then place her under heavy pressure to go further than she would freely choose. It may be only later that she realizes that what had been for her a peripheral concession, an expression of affection or appreciation, had been interpreted by him as an invitation to full satisfaction. What may be to the male an obvious and very desirable activity may be to the female *at that juncture* a quite superfluous and even repugnant step to which she only reluctantly agrees and which she may later regret. An experience which the man may be able to shrug off without embarrassment or distress may be the source of considerable pain and anguish to the woman. Such experiences are less common as women come to accept both their own sensuality *and* their right to put a firm limit to male importunity; but I find that significant numbers of college women get unnecessarily hurt because men fail to be sensitive to their real interests.

In reporting a study of 1,200 college students conducted by the Kinsey Institute, Gebhard noted that while "it is becoming respectable to be an admittedly sexually responsive female" and "the female today is regarded less as a sexual object to be exploited and more as a human being with rights to sexual expression," there remain striking differences between men and women in their attitudes to intercourse. "Females surrender their virginity to males they love, whereas males are much less emotionally involved." A much higher percentage of women nowadays enjoy their first experience of coitus, and fewer than in the past feel any embarrassment or guilt. But whereas 50–60 percent of the women interviewed said their first experience was with someone they loved and planned to marry, only 11–14 percent of the males said they loved and planned to marry their first sexual partner (*The New York Times*, December 30, 1967). There was no one-for-one correlation between these subjects, but the discrepancy suggests that a large number of the women had evaluated the quality of the relationship very differently from their male partners. As Ramsey has pointed out:

Gebhard noted the "enormous difference between how males and females view their initial partner," and he summarily describes men as tending to be "opportunistic" about sex. This ought to be no surprise, although it apparently was to a high percentage of the young women questioned. Where was the "equality" in the attitudes and the personal integrity and relatedness to each other at the source of the enjoyments and non-enjoyments reported? (Ramsey, 1968).

On the other hand, once a relationship has reached a degree of depth, the woman may be happy to participate in intimacies she had previously resisted. "Her primary motive for engaging in coitus is not the gratification of her own sexuality but the gratification of her partner's out of her need to be loved," says Bardwick (1971, p. 51). Among college students "it is very clear that female eroticism is primarily psychological, primarily a function of wanting to love and secure love. When we ask why they make love, very very few ever answer because it is a pleasure for *them*. . . . For most, the sex act is important because the male makes it important; for these women, it tended not to be important in its own right" (ibid., pp. 54–55). The change in female attitude can be perplexing and sometimes upsetting for the male. Some men who want to marry a virgin consciously or unconsciously test their partners by trying to get them to agree to intercourse and then reject them if they eventually consent. The underlying dynamics may be, as Kirkendall (1961) suggests, that the male is rationalizing his own guilt by blaming the female whom he quite unfairly expects to act as his own conscience. But in any case misleading signals between the sexes remain a common source of unnecessary misunderstanding.

*   *   *

I believe that much confusion and suffering can be avoided if we are able to distinguish sexuality from sex, to integrate sexual relationships with interpersonal encounters as a whole, and to learn to be together with warmth and openness. If mutual self-growth becomes the goal rather than the achievement or granting of sexual favors the typical maneuvering for position, the need for deceptive covering, the inability to verbalize one's real desires and the consequent failures of communication that plague so much student sexual experience can be eliminated. So long as intercourse or orgasm is treated as an end in itself (whether one to be sought or denied), just so long will people be hurt, used, deceived, disappointed and stunted in their growth to sexual maturity. Sexuality should be a matter of joyous exploration, not of anxious grappling for positions. Men and women should be able to relax in the pleasure of growing personal and physical intimacy without a sense of pressure to reach orgasmic discharge. Kissing, fondling, caressing and petting should be enjoyed for their own value as means of interpersonal union, rather than checked off on a list of foothills to be scaled as quickly as possible before conquering Mount Climax.

The fundamental trust that is essential to any deep human relationship is undercut so long as either partner feels it necessary to put on a front, or fears that more will be asked than he or she is yet able to give. Each has to learn to put into words the real meaning of those silent signals, and to be prepared to respond to the hesitations, hopes, fears and joys of the other. The man must be able to admit his need of help in developing sexual sensitivity, and to be satisfied and happy with petting when the relationship does not require or cannot sustain coitus. The woman must be liberated to express her sexual needs, whether they be more or less genital than the man's, to communicate without apology how she feels about the relation of sex to affection or love and above all to value herself highly enough as a human being to feel no obligation to go along just in order to retain a man's affection. Both partners must escape from the current obsession with sex as a performance, in which the skill or response of the participants is measured as "success" or "failure." For so long as sex is used to demonstrate one's prowess or even one's sensitivity, and so long as one is afraid of being found "inadequate" in physical achievement, there is no real opening of the self to another, no freedom to trust, no truly mutual relationship.

Such an understanding of sexuality puts the question of intercourse in a new context. Different types of physical intimacy are appropriate for different degrees of communication and intimacy with a partner. The progression from kissing to necking, from necking to petting, from light to heavy petting and from petting to intercourse may be a natural, mutually accepted expression of a growing understanding and commitment. But in many cases the latter stages will never be reached, either because the relationship is broken off or because the relationship turns out to have limited physical sexual significance. Indeed, to speak of these "stages" as if they represented clearly defined way-stations on a journey to a specific destination, which alone gives them meaning, becomes inappropriate. The sensitivity and responsiveness of the whole body is appreciated for its own worth and given its proper valuation consistent with each relationship. Thus some people will continue for months, and perhaps for life, to enjoy kissing, fondling and hugging each other without any sense of pressure or obligation to engage in any genital contact. Others will find petting, with or without orgasm for either partner, a suitable expression of their affection.

That this kind of experience is possible is shown by the increasingly common practice of students sleeping together without having intercourse. "Many college students," states one experienced observer, "are now aware that one does not have to insert a penis into a vagina in order to have a pleasant and emotionally gratifying relationship with a partner" (Coons, 1972). A survey on one campus found that two out of every three responding students had slept with a member of the other sex all night without engaging in coitus. Macklin (1972) reports that some couples at Cornell had lived together for as long as three months without intercourse because they did not yet feel ready for this experience. In an article discussing the ways in which open sexuality can contribute to the personal growth of men and women at college, Madison (1971) quotes this example:

I used to see her each day when she'd come over to eat; finally, I asked her out—a turning point in my life. . . . Linda taught me to appreciate art, drama and certain forms of music and introduced me to many new ideas taken from her studies— studies that I would never have come in contact with myself. In turn, I taught her to appreciate hikes and picnics and getting close to nature. I even took her fishing with me a couple of times; she loved it. She painted and I fished; usually she had better luck than I did.

We saw each other constantly, but grew into love slowly. Our lovemaking reached peaks that I had never before experienced, nor have I since. You will not believe this, but we never had intercourse in the 14 months we went together. We didn't think twice about going to bed nude and staying there for hours, but she didn't want intercourse. I think she was afraid to say that if she became pregnant before graduating, she would destroy her parents, as they had sacrificed so much to put her through, so I didn't push her. We'd just lie there for hours talking, caressing, and being with each other. . . . The funny thing is that while we never had intercourse, it didn't matter. I always felt satisfied anyway, as long as I was with her.

Norman O. Brown (1959) has popularized the somewhat unfortunate Freudian phrase "polymorphous perversity" to express this concept of total bodily sexuality, in contrast to the goal-oriented attitude which has for so long characterized Western culture. He believes it involves a recovery of the natural sexuality of childhood:

Infantile sexuality is the pursuit of pleasure obtained through the activity of any and all organs of the human body. So defined, the ultimate essence of our desires and our being is nothing more or less than delight in the active life of all the human body (p. 30).

The process of sublimation encouraged by civilization has restricted sexuality to the genitals and deflected libido into other, more acceptable and useful channels. However, Brown does not think that such a repression of natural sexuality is unalterable; indeed he argues that because it remains part of the self (particularly evidenced in sexual fantasy) there is always the potential for recovery. "The hidden aim of sublimation and the cultural process is the progressive discovery of the lost body of childhood" (ibid., p. 170). There is a way out from the cumulative repression, guilt and aggression resulting from the conflict between baffled instincts and the desexualized world and self: "con-

sciousness embracing and affirming instinctual reality—
Dionysian consciousness" (ibid., p. 176).

Brown speaks of a "resurrection of the body," not in
traditional terms, but such that "the human body would
become polymorphously perverse, delighting in that full
life of all the body which it now fears" (ibid., p. 308). He
pictures a "Dionysian or body mysticism" (in contrast to
the Apollonian world-denying mysticism of much religious
tradition) which "stays with life, which is the body, and
seeks to transform and perfect it," finding a way out of the
human neurosis into "that simple health that animals enjoy, but not man" (ibid., pp. 310–11). *Love's Body* (1966)
is a subtle and often confusing collection of quotations
and reflections covering a vast range of material in literature, mythology, history, psychoanalysis, religion, anthro-
pology and poetry. The book reflects Brown's often ir-
reverent obsession with such words as penis, erection,
semen, vagina, hymen, masturbation, castration and coitus.
Its proclamation of a new consciousness, an erotic sense of
reality and the resurrection and unity of the body containing both sexes has encouraged its readers to interpret it in
terms of the "polymorphous perversity" of the earlier work.
Brown has been claimed by many as a prophet of recreational sex, a celebrant of sensual play as an end in itself.
But despite his exuberant use of genital language he has a
far broader understanding of sexuality and the sensuous.

"Polymorphous perversity in the literal, physical sense is
not the real issue," Brown has said. "I don't like the suggestion that polymorphous perversity of the imagination
is somehow second-best to literal polymorphous perversity.
. . . Polymorphous perversity turns out to be a poetical
rather than a literal thing. It is a form of mental playful-
ness as in *Finnegans Wake,* something I do with my mind,
a changed way of seeing that I would like to carry into

everything I see" (Bennis, 1970). It is *art* which "by over-coming the inhibition and by activating the playful primary process" provides relief from the pressures of reason, undoes repression and is thus subversive of civilization (Brown, 1959, p. 63). What is needed is that men attain their proper perfection as an animal species and recover the power of sensual *speech* (ibid., p. 73). Most significantly, when discussing the nature of the Dionysian consciousness, Brown illustrates it by reference to Isadora Duncan's experience of ecstasy as "the defeat of the intelligence," and implies that she wrongly identified the Dionysian experience with the orgasm. "The Dionysian ego," says Brown, "would be freed from genital organization. . . . While the Apollonian ego is the ego of genital organization, the Dionysian ego would be once more a body-ego and would not have to be dissolved in body-rapture" (ibid., p. 176). In other words, Brown is warning us *against* orgasm worship and urging the recovery of the sensual as a continuum from speech to total body feeling. He would be the last to isolate the genital from the wider range of sexuality or the body from the mind and the imagination.

On the other hand it would be quite mistaken to interpret Brown as repudiating the pleasure of intercourse and orgasm. Herbert W. Richardson (1971), claiming to present a view of the eroticization of society similar to that of Brown, endorses the ascetic practices of the nineteenth century Oneida Community. This utopian group practiced a method of sexual union called *maithuna,* or male continence, "a method of avoiding ejaculation and *male* orgasm." Richardson claims that this odd accomplishment "totally transforms the meaning and purpose of the sexual act," shifting it "from excitation and tension release—a purely private pleasure—to the continued communion, heightened mutual awareness, and shared enjoyment of the partners" (ibid., p. 132). But he totally fails to recognize the profoundly interpersonal quality of orgasmic experience between lovers, and his eroticized society turns out in the end to be based on the *repudiation* of the physical in favor of a traditional religious assertion of the supremacy of the intellect and the will. Mature sexuality does not make intercourse and orgasm a goal, but neither does it exclude the unique and supreme satisfaction of mutual orgasmic pleasure.*

Here is a description of a woman student's discovery of the wonder of sexuality. From a condition of fear, guilt, shame and uncertainty in her freshman year she was able, as a result of the patience and understanding of a man, to develop a positive appreciation of the sensual:

I spent the summer following my freshman year in college in Bermuda, and it proved to be the most educational few months I have ever experienced. . . . I met Ray. . . . His fight for independence from his parents was really causing him trouble. . . . Immediately, I was full of feelings for him. . . . I sensed that he needed somebody, and I wanted very much to be the object of his dependence. . . .

We went everywhere together, and a mutual understanding grew. I loved all of the adventures we had—surfing, shopping, sleeping on the beach, skin diving, or climbing to a mountain

---

* This does *not* mean the mythical "simultaneous orgasm" so often promoted by the sex manuals and so persistently and pointlessly sought by young (and old) lovers. While those who happen on the experience can surely be thankful for it, it is more likely to be a disappointment than a satisfaction if it is sought as a goal. The difference of arousal patterns between two partners makes it likely that an attempt to orchestrate orgasmic release will result in anxiety and frustration. Indeed authorities are increasingly saying that simultaneous orgasm may be less pleasurable since concern with the needs of the partner can detract from the enjoyment of one's own fulfillment. Sequential orgasm is as truly mutual (given the appropriate context of personal relationship) as simultaneous orgasm.

pool to swim. Soon it turned out to be quite convenient if I would sign out for weekends and merely stay with him. We worked and lived together. As before, affection and sex entered into the situation. He did not push me, and I began to lose that ugly fear. Our relationship was really turning into something wonderful. Then he began to expect more and more. I wanted to be able to give and love him. Yet this idea of morals that had plagued me and always been there arose. We had many arguments about it but I just couldn't. Once we came very close to intercourse, but I suddenly felt great fear and began sobbing and crying. Ray . . . would sit down and try to explain and make me understand how he felt and how he thought. . . . Ray was the first person to make me understand that morals are a personal, circumstantial type of thing rather than blind, hard-and-fast rules. It changed me a great deal. . . . I ended up staying an extra month in Bermuda (Madison, 1971).

Despite all the assumptions to the contrary in literature, movies, sex manuals and dormitory conversations, it cannot be emphasized strongly enough that early experiences of intercourse are *not* by any means always satisfactory for the man. This is particularly true when either partner agrees to the act with serious reservations or out of a sense of obligation to fulfill an expected role. After the great build-up of fantasy the man's first attempts at coitus may be less pleasurable than masturbation. A partly dilated hymen or a vagina tensed by anxiety or pain may make penetration difficult or impossible. Premature ejaculation* before full intromission of the penis in the vagina is common among young men highly excited by achieving the vaunted "goal" of intercourse. Impotence, or failure to

---

* Both premature ejaculation and impotence are likely to be of emotional rather than physical origin. Alcohol or other drugs can, however, cause temporary impotence.

have an erection or maintain it long enough to achieve penetration, may be due to unconscious fears of failure to "perform" adequately, or to unadmitted questions about engaging in intercourse.

If sexuality is understood as I have been suggesting these problems are much less likely to arise, and if they do their consequences will be far less traumatic. If a couple are used to enjoying each other's bodies in a variety of expressions of intimacy, and if intercourse is simply the last of a series of mutually enjoyable experiences rather than a target or a concession, premature ejaculation and impotence are far less likely to occur. If there exists a good level of open communication between the partners their occurrence can be recognized without embarrassment or feelings of failure. Either can ask for or offer manual or oral stimulation if necessary. What is totally absurd is to imagine that some serious abnormality exists, or that the relationship is worthless because the first few attempts at intercourse prove less than earthshaking.

Problems associated with the first experiences of intercourse for the woman can also be greatly reduced if the context is one of relaxed confidence preceded by earlier, less demanding sexual activities. If intercourse is part of a growing together rather than an objective to be rushed or a challenge to be met, early physical problems can be discussed with understanding between the partners, rather than becoming possible causes of embarrassment, disappointment or recrimination. The fact that the woman may be at a stage of her menstrual cycle at which she is less able to respond physically can be taken into account.* If there

* That every woman has times in the cycle at which she is more likely to enjoy orgasm is generally agreed; but which phase is the most erotic for any individual cannot be anticipated. Sherfey (1972) thinks the last fourteen days (between ovulation and menstruation) likely to be the most

is inadequate vaginal lubrication or a minor infection, postponement can be agreed on until a suitable lubricant (KY Jelly is the most widely used) or medication is obtained.

A woman is likely to find her first coitus far from enjoyable if she is unsure of the emotional involvement of the man, if there is anxiety about being disturbed or becoming pregnant, if she has serious doubts about premarital intercourse or if their love-making is peremptory. The common reason for women failing to enjoy orgasm during intercourse is not ignorance about the best "position." There is no magical way of interlocking bodies that can guarantee pleasure. The most important factor is the sensitivity of the partner, and his readiness to respond to her need for stimulation, which will often require his patient cooperation for some time after he has reached a climax.* Once again, mutual recognition of the need for manual or oral arousal in addition to the act of intercourse is essential. If the man expects the woman to be immediately satisfied merely by the movement of his penis in her vagina he has an inadequate understanding of female sexuality. And if she

---

responsive; but others (Cavanagh, 1969; Morris and Udry, 1971) have found women more easily aroused in the post-menstrual period or at ovulation.

* Some women who have enjoyed orgasm during masturbation are slower to become orgasmic in intercourse than those who have not masturbated. The reason may be that they have expectations that are not immediately met. Masters and Johnson reported (1966) that many women found masturbatory orgasm more intense (though often less satisfying) than orgasm during intercourse. The reason is probably that in masturbation there is direct and carefully controlled massage of the clitoral area, whereas in coitus the clitoral hood is only indirectly affected by the movement of the penis pulling on the labia minora (Sherfey, 1972). Thus a woman used to masturbation may take some time to adjust to the different tempo of intercourse and often (perhaps always) will continue to need direct clitoral-area stimulation.

does not feel free to take an active part in love-making and explain what movements and touches are most stimulating the necessary confidence for a satisfying relationship is lacking. Seaman (1971) reports that certain complaints about male sexual behavior were repeated by many of her subjects, despite their very varied tastes: "Men make love as if they are following a program. . . . They are humorless. . . . They are too fast. . . . They are cruel to women who require finger stimulation, making them feel that this is a loathsome aberration. . . . They are interested in the "target" organs only, and they fail to appreciate the total body sensuality of women. . . . And, above all, they ignore the woman's statements about what she likes" (p. 90).

Of course, there will be disappointment and pain even with the best will in the world. One of the problematic things about sexuality is that two people, however responsive to each other, seldom develop their mutual personal and physical involvement at the same tempo. Most people go through experiences in which, even with the most sincere effort at honest communication and the most careful concern to avoid undue pressure, one becomes more deeply committed than the other. Sometimes with patience the imbalance rights itself, but often the outcome is conflict and eventual separation. You can't be sexually intimate with another human being, whether intercourse is involved or not, without the possibility of wounding or being wounded. But the pain and disillusion arising when an honest human relationship is terminated are quite different from those that may follow from a situation of sexual exploitation, promiscuity or deceit.

It is one thing to find that someone for whom you have affection or love cannot continue to share that quality of involvement. It is a far more damaging experience to discover that someone who declared affection or love never really felt it. It is one thing to share your body with some-one in the course of a mutual journey of self-discovery. It is quite another thing to do so under pressure, on the basis of false assurances of love or under a sense of obligation which overrides your deepest convictions. It is one thing to explore the pleasures of sex as part of a human relation-ship. It is something else to treat one's genitals or those of a partner as a mere subject of curious experimentation divorced from the whole feeling, thinking, relating person. In each case the dishonest, coercive, impersonal alterna-tive may well leave a heritage of guilt, repugnance or self-disgust. The other experience, while still painful, involves no lowering of self-esteem and may well be a positive con-tribution to the adequate appreciation of sexuality and to emotional growth.

CHAPTER VI

Love and Commitment

Many students justify sexual intimacy, particularly intercourse, on the principle "Love makes it right, so long as nobody gets hurt." *"If we deeply love one another,"* wrote one man, "and we find in sex a way of showing its deepest levels; if we find that during and after and because of it we are both straining to grow in stature in the other's eyes; if we find that because it is loving, the release of the sex energy also releases, rather than uses up, our deepest creative energies; if each time there is a sexual interlude, we find we love and respect and admire each other more afterwards, then, and only then, but so sensitively and wonderfully then, *it is right"* (Kronhausen and Kronhausen, 1960, p. 228).

But many others, who would as firmly repudiate the use of sex for purely recreational purposes without personal involvement, find that the word love carries connotations or implications they do not think essential for full sexual intimacy. Lower (1973) quotes one woman student as saying that formerly she would have said that intercourse was all right only for couples who were in love, "but now I'm twenty-two, it is all right for those who simply *share* affection. The reason for this change is that I'm not sure what love is" (p. 73). Reiss (1967) found that whereas 19 percent of the students in his sample endorsed "permissiveness with affection," less than half of these (9 percent) felt that engagement or love was necessary as a justification for intercourse.

Affection may be the best term to describe a degree of personal concern, openness, lack of coercion and communication that is less fully developed than love, but a meaningful basis for all types of sexual intimacy. For insofar as sexuality is an important element in the development of emotional security, intimacy, trust and self-identity it precedes the capacity for mature love. An individual's capacity to make the kind of commitment he or she means by "love" may only come into being as a result of sexual experience —including intercourse—through which mutual affection and interpersonal relationship are given expression. Sex with a purely physical goal is not likely to be the basis of creative growth,* but where there is honest respect for the partner, the will to relate as human beings, a couple who are close and affectionate may well find that intercourse is creative of love.

Kirkendall (1961) suggests that these principles offer a minimal guide by which to test whether an act of sexual intimacy is justified:

Whenever a decision or a choice is to be made concerning behavior, *the moral decision will be the one which works toward the creation of trust, confidence, and integrity in relationships.* It should increase the capacity of individuals to cooperate, and

---

* It *can* be, however. The attempt to divorce the physical from the emotional in sex is never entirely successful. The mere readiness of one individual to give and receive physical satisfaction from another, provided there is no dissembling, may constitute a first glimmer of affection. Paul Goodman in an interview in *Psychiatry Today* (1971) claimed that many of his close friendships originated in purely physical sexual encounters.

enhance the sense of self-respect in the individual. Acts which create distrust, suspicion, and misunderstanding, which build barriers and destroy integrity, are immoral. They decrease the individual's sense of self-respect, and rather than producing a capacity to work together they separate people and break down the capacity for communication (p. 6, my emphasis).

The problem with invoking "love" as a prerequisite is its strong association in our culture with "romantic love." Romantic love was originally regarded by religious and secular authorities as a moral threat but Western society now regards it not only as acceptable, but as a desirable condition for marriage. Now that the power of religious dogma has declined and fears of pregnancy and venereal disease are no longer effective deterrents against premarital intercourse, the association of love, sex and marriage has become a tenet of faith. As we noted in Chapter 3, religious authorities generally argue for premarital chastity on the ground that the ultimate sexual intimacy should be preserved for the ultimate commitment of love in marriage. But many who do not buy that argument are still deeply influenced by the association of love, sex and marriage.

A couple may assume that *because* they are "in love" they are adequately prepared for marriage: the tragedy of divorce following the majority of teenage marriages exposes the fallacy. A woman may persuade herself that *because* she's gotten deeply involved to the point of intercourse, she must be in love—and then find it impossible to be honest about the real quality of the relationship. A man may find self-confidence and independence through a relationship with a woman, but if he *assumes* that the warmth of the experience necessarily constitutes love he may find himself unable to terminate the involvement when its value has been fulfilled. "I'm in love: I must get married." "I'm sexually excited: I must be in love." "I'm in love: I must have intercourse." These are three common fallacies that lead to misunderstanding and hurt. Conrad's dictum "No man fully understands his own artful dodges to escape from the grim shadow of selfknowledge" is particularly relevant to our sexual lives. It is the easiest thing in the world to be persuaded that one is "in love." One senior admitted to Greene that "some of us manage to fall in love two or three times a week."

I am not among those who regard romantic love as an emotional disorder: studies to date do not indicate any correlation between romantic love and neurotic personality traits (Kephart, 1973). When a psychologist writes an article entitled "This Thing Called Love Is Pathological" (Casler, 1969) and tells us that "the person who is secure, independent, and has a satisfying sex life will not need to love," he seems to me to be falling into the same fallacy of oversimplification as leads the person who "falls in love" to assume that he or she is ready for marriage. Romantic love is a joyful, liberating, ecstatic emotion that gives new meaning to life and transforms one's world. Three out of every four people say it has made their lives happier (Kephart, 1973), and there is no evidence that it adversely affects the prospects for successful marriage (Spanier, 1972). Through it many are lifted out of the narrow self-concern of adolescence and caught up in a relationship which has at least the seeds of maturity in it. The fact that the beloved is endowed with idealized, exaggerated qualities is not necessarily "merely a madness" in Shakespeare's cynical terms. We should recognize the possibility, as Maslow (1962) suggests, that the lover is able to perceive realities to which others are blind, because the perceptive powers of a person in love are heightened.

But this does not alter the fact that romantic love in itself is immature and inadequate unless it is balanced by rational and critical insights. Its joys are not to be scorned or despised; but its mere presence is no guarantee of personal strength or a stable relationship. It may be the precursor of adult love, but its characteristics and potential distortions need to be recognized before it can develop into a solid basis for mature sexuality or marriage. Romantic love tends to attribute to one, usually temporary, relationship a finality and exclusiveness which general human experience shows to be unrealistic.

As a matter of sheer fact the great majority of people do *not* find complete fulfillment for life with the first boy or girl they fall in love with. Yet in romantic love it is assumed that the first relationship will certainly bring perfect happiness, and last forever. Contrary to all the evidence it is believed that the beloved is the one and only possible partner, and that a couple's intuitive conviction that they are "made for each other" is beyond question or doubt. Romantic lovers assume that all their problems will be resolved with time, that all disagreements or incompatibilities will disappear if they stay together and that any apparent deficiencies in the partner will be magically corrected if only they get married. They resent any attempt by others to make them face reality, and indeed a recent study has shown that the intensity of romantic love is related to the degree of parental opposition it evokes. In what the authors called the "Romeo and Juliet Effect" obstacles raised by the family markedly increased the desirability of the relationship for the couple (Driscoll, et al., 1972).

Romantic love is very often sexually goal-oriented. "Love makes it right" means, quite simply, "Love makes intercourse right." The "Romeo and Juliet Effect" comes into play again, and because it is specifically coitus that is prohibited by our society the whole relationship is geared especially towards genital consummation and the wider range of sexuality is downgraded. The ritual of chasing and being chased, of titillating and satisfying, replaces free communication between human persons. Germaine Greer (1971) writes bitterly but persuasively of "the wretched cant" of love, "masking egotism, lust, masochism, fantasy under a mythology of sentimental postures, a welter of self-induced miseries and joys, blinding and masking the essential personalities in the frozen gestures of courtship, in the kissing and the dating and the desire, the compliments and the quarrels which vivify its barrenness" (p. 165). The relaxed enjoyment of the other person as a sexual *person* can be lost in the passionate desire to enjoy him or her as a sexual *object*. Energy and enthusiasm can be so focused on the satisfaction of the body that the opportunity for communication and interchange of ideas and interests of a non-sexual type is minimized. A couple who have enjoyed a totally absorbing romantic affair may at the end of three or six months know no more about each other on any level than the physical than they did at the beginning.

Romantic love is, to a considerable extent, self-love. The lover projects upon the other person the ideal qualities that he desires. "We all know that the beloved as regarded by the lover is not identical with the person seen by everyone else: and that falling in love involves an over-valuation and a distorted picture of the person who is loved. To us a girl may seem ordinary: to him she 'walks in beauty like the night.' To us a man appears commonplace: to her he is a romantic hero" (Storr, 1963, p. 121). Stendahl put it with acuity: "Even the most prudent person, from the very moment he or she is in love, ceases to see an object as it really is. He underrates his own advantages and overestimates the slightest favor of the beloved creature. . . . In all the other passions it is the desire that must be adapted to cold reality; here the reality is hurriedly molded to the shape of the desire."

This idealization of the beloved may have its positive value, as I suggested above. As one looks in wonder at the capacity of very unattractive people to arouse the passionate devotion of other individuals one is bound to reflect that apart from this capacity few could enjoy the experience of love. But it can reflect a fundamental insecurity, a sense of personal inadequacy which is crippling, a need for a relationship which is not one of mutual respect but one of absorption. This may be a normal phase of growth in adolescence, when self-esteem has to be established through love, when the partners are helping each other to achieve self-identity. But it represents a very transitory stage of development, and a precarious foundation for any permanent commitment.

Paradoxically, romantic love expresses itself in excessive dependence and possessiveness at the same time: the beloved person is adored as perfection itself, but because that ideal is so essential to the existence of the lover its loss is feared above all else. It is the former that Casler (1969) rightly warns against when he calls love "pathological." "To the extent that love fosters dependency, it may be viewed as a deterrent to maturity . . . the person who seeks love in order to obtain security will become, like the alcoholic, increasingly dependent on this source of illusory well-being."

Here is an example of a man who has so idolized his love that he seems to have lost all sense of independent value: "There's a magnetism between us. If I lost her I'd sort of die, I'd go mad. I'm sometimes afraid that she might go off with someone else, but I don't think she would. If I search for years, a million years, I'd never find anyone like her. She's all I live for, all I work for. . . . I can't go wrong with her" (Hamblett and Deverson, 1964, p. 77). Most of us have probably felt something like that about someone; we've discovered eventually that he or she is not the embodiment of every virtue, and we have survived the discovery, however painfully. But to enter a lifelong union, as so many have done in the past, on the basis of a mirage is to invite disaster.

The man just quoted manifests another tendency of romantic love—possessiveness. There is a lack of real trust in the other person (despite her supreme qualities) arising from a basic anxiety about the possibility of losing her. Just because she is so absolutely necessary the fear of her being attracted to someone else is too much to face: it would mean death. Yet because he lacks confidence in himself and cannot imagine that this creature of perfection really wants him, he cannot quite trust her to love him. Possessiveness therefore leads to jealousy, the claim to exclusive rights, the refusal to allow the romantic dream figure to have an independent existence.

"The terms of such passion are all negative," writes Greer (1971). " 'I never wanted anyone but you: you're the only woman I've ever loved' is taken as sufficient justification for undisputed possession. Because the lover cannot live without his beloved she must remain with him even against her will. And this is most often recognized as love. As long as the beloved stays she may be treated with great generosity but once she leaves she is an object of hatred and reprisal" (p. 150). The reverse sexism of the passage is justified. Women have been taught to be the less jealous (and, despite the venerable myth, the less romantic) lovers because they have been obliged to accept the fact that they do not and will not possess their men entirely. The double standard, far from dead, expects that women be virgins at marriage and allows men to sow their wild oats. It has been men who have reacted most violently to the possibility that the women they love might have sexual relationships with another man.

I believe that the current questioning of the association of sex, love and marriage is entirely sound, both individually and socially. Today's students are not, as we have seen, indifferent to the relation between sex and affection or love. They are not generally satisfied with recreational sex. Nor are they indifferent to the ideal of marriage as a commitment to one partner. Although students reject the traditional view of home and family as the be-all and end-all for women (Epstein and Bronzaft, 1972), the great majority look forward eventually to marriage (Luckey and Nass, 1969). But they are critical of the state of marriage as they observe it in adult society, and they rightly perceive that a primary source of marital disaster has been the fact that people have married in the haze of romantic passion, under external or internal pressure to provide a publicly approved context for sexual fulfillment, and without the personal maturity and mutual understanding that can form the basis for permanent commitment and parental obligations. They want to ensure, as far as possible, that when they make such a commitment it will have a reasonable chance of success. They want to enjoy sexuality without the rigid demarcations between virginity and non-virginity that official society still pays lip service to. While they are frequently caught up in the excitement and exhilaration of romantic love they see through its more unrealistic and neurotic aspects and want to graduate to adult love before entering into any permanent marriage.

For many students, living together on or off campus seems to offer the best prospect for achieving mature sexuality and adult love. It does not involve the finality of a marital commitment, but it makes possible a truly personal relationship rather than a series of purely sexual interludes. A study of those who had engaged in living together found that more than half rated the relationship "very successful" and eight out of ten thought it "maturing and pleasant." None found it detrimental to their personal growth and a majority even of those whose relationship had come to an end declared that they would do it again with the same person (Macklin, 1972).

At the same time, living together has its difficulties, and those students who consider it (reportedly four out of five: Arafat and Yorburg, 1973b) should be aware of them. One woman who had lived with her lover for two years at college remarked that "many of the same things have to be taken into account before entering this type of arrangement as should be considered before entering marriage" ("Living Together on Campus," *Sexology*, September 1970). She pointed out that once it becomes a way of life severing the relationship can be emotionally disrupting; on the other hand the very fact that it is not regarded as permanent may breed insecurities in those involved. And she expressed the fear that "the unsatisfactory break-up of a relationship can cause a girl to desperately—and futilely —seek other relationships in hopes of resolving her insecurities or anxieties."

Macklin (1972) found that "the major emotional problem was the tendency to become over-involved and to feel a subsequent loss of identity, lack of opportunity to participate in other activities or be with friends, and an overdependency on the relationship." She raised the question whether the level of student self-identity is sufficiently high to make even a semi-permanent commitment advisable at this stage of personal development.

The difference between male and female expectations may be a significant factor in these relationships. One study found that while few gave marriage as the primary reason for living together "males were half as likely to list future marriage rather than sexual gratification as a primary reason . . . and females were almost half as likely as males to list sexual gratification as a primary motive" (Arafat and Yorburg, 1973b). Thirty-six percent of the males gave sexual gratification as the first reason for living together: "It's less of a hassle to get laid," said one. "Sex—when you want it, where you want it," said another. Where the decision to live together is based on such goal-oriented sexual interests I question whether there is sufficient maturity to make it likely that the experience will be truly rewarding. Ingrid Bengis (1972) discovered that her attachments to men usually deepened, whereas theirs seemed to lessen: "I didn't realize that sex made a difference, or at least not that *kind* of a difference. I thought sex was an expression of love, a part of love. What I didn't think was that it transformed everything, that for me and for most women, making love with a man several times created unpredictable bonds—which weren't broken by saying: 'THIS WAS A TRIAL MARRIAGE FOR WHICH THE CONTRACT HAS EXPIRED.' I didn't realize that intimacy, physical intimacy, had unknown properties, that it created deepening needs, created highly unprogressive bursts of possessiveness and jealousy, created some balance between tension and satisfaction that became the mirror of every other aspect of a relationship" (pp. 200–201).

But whatever the problems, I believe that today's students can hardly do worse than my generation has done, and that the outcome of their new freedom may well result in much happier marriages in the future and richer lives for the unmarried. I cannot see that society will do much good by ignoring or deploring the situation. Arafat and Yorburg (1973b) found that 80 percent of the students at a large northeastern university declared that they would live with a member of the opposite sex, without marriage, given the opportunity to do so. Rather than moralizing about the importance of premarital chastity we would do better to encourage experimentation that will enable people to grow up with a non-competitive, non-illusory attitude to sexuality and love.

In particular we should do all in our power to ensure that information and resources for birth control are available for all students. One theme of this book is the responsibility of each individual, or each couple, to determine what is responsible behavior. We have long passed the point at which people are going to listen to religious or secular authorities claiming to specify acceptable sexual acts. But there is one principle that I think can and must be affirmed: *Thou shalt not conceive an unwanted child.* What are the rights or wrongs of premarital or non-marital intercourse must be judged in the context of the intention, honesty and concern of the persons involved. But no situation, I suggest, can justify carelessness or indifference about contraception.* And if this is so, society has a responsibility to provide the means for any person of any age to take the necessary precautions against pregnancy. There is no evidence to show that birth control information leads to increased sexual irresponsibility: indeed it clearly reduces it —for reducing the number of acts of intercourse resulting in unwanted conception far outweighs any possible harm resulting from an increase in the total number of acts of extramarital intercourse.

*   *   *

Having recognized the limitations of romantic love we must now attempt to identify the qualities of love in which

* I owe this point to Rabbi Eugene Borowitz (Borowitz, 1969).

the sexual and the emotional find their ultimate integration. Few people ever achieve full maturity in sexuality and love, but the serious student will hope to grow throughout the years on campus, and can at least seek to develop these qualities in the course of successive experiences. Storr (1964) suggests the ideal to which we can approximate:

Sexual intercourse may be said to be one aspect, perhaps the most basic and most important aspect, of a relationship between persons. In ideally mature form it is a relationship between a man and a woman in which giving and taking is equal, and in which the genitals are the most important channel through which love is expressed and received. It is one of the most natural, and certainly the most rewarding and the most life-enhancing of all human experiences. It is also the only one which both has a completely satisfying ending and yet can be endlessly repeated. Not even the greatest works of literature and music can stand such iteration. But this wonderfully enriching experience is only possible when the two people concerned have achieved a relationship in which, at least during the actual process of love-making, each is able to confront the other exactly as they are, with no reserves and no pretences, and in which there is no admixture of childish dependence or fear (p. 14).

The first essential quality of love is the absence of make-believe or illusion. The misleading signals of the dating game are gone and the couple no longer feel it necessary to pretend they are other than they are, to present an external beauty or power they do not possess or to attempt to control the situation for fear of being found out. The partner is appreciated and loved not only for what he or she can give and share but for what he or she *is*. Sexual love certainly includes a profound pleasure in the physical qualities of the beloved, and the consummate enjoyment of intercourse and orgasm. But love also respects, admires and serves because of other qualities—courge, compassion, imagination, patience, integrity, vivacity and sympathy.

Love, as Fromm (1956) puts it, is "the active concern for the life and growth of that which we love"—a concern that finds expression in care, responsibility, respect and true knowledge of the other (p. 22). The concept of "caring" has been elaborated by Mayeroff (1971): "To care for another person, in the most significant sense, is to help him grow and actualize himself. . . . Caring is the antithesis of simply using the other person to satisfy one's own needs. . . . In helping the other grow I do not impose my own direction; rather, I allow the direction of the other's growth to guide what I do, to help determine how I am to respond and what is relevant to such response" (pp. 1, 7).

When we romantically love someone we make them in the image we construct to meet our compulsive need. Where this distortion dominates, a true relationship is impossible, for we cannot afford to face the human realities of the person we idolize. Some partial distortion is never entirely absent, but in adult love it is the awareness of capacities in the beloved that are present but have not been fully realized—not qualities we have projected out of our own imagination. Consequently it is possible to see the other person clearly, aware of their imperfections but still lovable. "If our relationship is a progressive thing, not merely a static achievement, we may approximate to a stage in which, because each fulfills the other's need, each is also treated as a whole person by the other. Whereas formerly two people in love served only to complete what each felt to be lacking—now two whole people confront each other as individuals" (Storr, 1963, p. 125). The true lover is able to accept the partner as he is: not uncritically, not without any desire to see change, but without wanting to mold the person in his own image. "Love lets the other be," says Laing (1967), "but with affection and concern. Violence attempts to constrain the other's freedom, to force him to act in the way we desire, but with ultimate lack of concern, with indifference to the other's own existence or destiny" (p. 36).

Barbara Seaman (1972) calls this experience of sexual love "transcendent sex" because it is "an almost mystical experience of renewal, where body and soul seem to be perfectly integrated, existence is given meaning and immortality is somehow affirmed." One such experience, she declares, makes a permanent difference, leaving the man or woman "more spontaneous, more open, more confident, more loving, more purposeful and more peaceful." But she points out that it is all too easy to revert to less than fully adult sex, and indeed to some extent we all do so. "In peak moments, one lover enters fully into the heart and understanding of the other, affirming him as the particular person he is, saying yes to him. But this must be a two-way process. When monologue masquerades as dialogue, when we try to appear what we are not, or when we treat the other as an 'it,' we are not true lovers. We deceive and are deceived, and sex becomes, at best, a rather enjoyable indoor sport, at worst, a travesty and an evil" (p. 191).

But mature love not only values the other as a real and independent person: it is also based on a respect for oneself. Even in the most demanding ethical imperative we are exhorted to "love your neighbor *as yourself*"—not *instead of* yourself. The man or woman who has no confidence or security about his or her worth as a person and as a sexual being has nothing to give to or share with the partner.

He who is able to love himself is able to love others also, for he has understood his true value and does not need to bolster up his own value by snatching it from others. When I am unaware of what I truly am I am incapable of giving myself value, and so I desperately seek value from someone else; and this leads me to action which is sometimes identified with sex; but with sex divorced from its true object, which is the completion of the union of two people who have found their own value, and therefore found value in each other (Rhymes, 1964, p. 34).

The person who is guilty or ashamed about his sexual nature cannot enter into free and mutual self-giving because he cannot believe that anyone really sees something in him to love. One who doubts his identity as a person, who is fearful of absorption, who retains a childish dependence on the other, cannot afford to risk true intimacy for fear that his inadequacies will be uncovered and his false security destroyed.* For such a person a deep and intimate love relation is a threat, a challenge to self-exposure or self-surrender which is seen as involving potential hurt or destruction.

There is a certain defenselessness and even death in sexuality. May (1969) recounts a patient's problem with inability to enjoy intercourse, and a dream in which she had the conviction that she would have to jump into a river and drown, resulting in great anxiety. But the same night she had an orgasm during intercourse for the first time. "Something very basic had taken place in this woman's

* The use of the masculine pronoun in these two sentences is purely a convenience. Bardwick (1971) believes that the cultural norms of our society reinforce the tendency for girls to continue in the affectional dependent relationships of childhood, and that "the American girl rarely achieves an independent sense of self and self-esteem" (p. 17).

dream—the capacity to confront death, a capacity which is a prerequisite to growth, a prerequisite to self-consciousness. I take the orgasm here as a psychological symbol of the capacity to abandon one's self, to give up present security in favor of the leap toward deeper experience. It is not by accident that the orgasm often appears symbolically as death and rebirth" (pp. 103–4). The difference is that the person who is still insecure never takes that step; the man or woman who does faces the risk knowing that in love neither participant loses self-identity or integrity. All of one's self can be invested because the other is trusted and the self is respected. In what Maslow (1962) calls "being-love," the lovers are "more independent of each other, more autonomous, less jealous or threatened, less needful, more individual, more distinterested, but also simultaneously more eager to help the other toward self-actualization, more proud of his triumphs, more altruistic, generous and fostering" (p. 40).

If love involves a truly mutual relationship it also implies a degree of mutual need. Without being jealously possessive each knows that he or she holds a unique place in the life of the other. In caring, says Mayeroff (1971), "I do not try to help the other grow in order to actualize myself, but by helping the other grow I do actualize myself" (p. 30). The ability to receive as well as to give is essential to the love relationship:

If you cannot receive, your giving will be a domination of the partner. Conversely, if you cannot give, your receiving will leave you empty. The paradox is demonstrably true that the person who can only receive becomes empty, for he is unable actively to appropriate and make his own what he receives. We speak, thus, not of receiving as a passive phenomenon, but of *active receiving:* one knows he is receiving, feels it, absorbs it into his own experience whether he verbally acknowledges it or not, and is grateful for it (May, 1969, p. 315).

In their understandable eagerness to correct the self-centered, jealous possessiveness of romantic love students not infrequently affirm that true love makes no restrictive claims on the partner, and that sexual relations are healthier if each is free to enjoy intimacy with others. Marriage is often dismissed as a hindrance to love because it limits spontaneity and puts a lien on the partner's affection. "Contemporary marriage," says one noted social scientist, "is a wretched institution. It spells the end of voluntary affection, of love freely given and joyously received" (Cadwallader, 1966). Love should be "without strings," concerned only with the good of the beloved and in no way assertive of one's own interests or rights. "The hallmark of egotistical love, even when it masquerades as altruistic love, is the negative answer to the question 'Do I want my love to be happy more than I want him to be with me?' " writes Greer (1971, pp. 156–57).

But this is surely another form of self-abnegation. To ignore one's own needs and worth is to subordinate one party in the relationship to the other. Indeed the theoretical question whether my love might be better off without me is strictly contradictory—for if he or she *loves* me my presence is important to us both. Of course it is all too possible that a relationship has decayed to the point that separation is right for the good of one or both of those involved: but in that case it is no longer a relationship of love in the full sense for it is no longer mutual. One cannot be a single lover; in this relationship above all one should not send to ask for whom the bell tolls. The lover, says Fromm (1956), "does not give in order to receive; giving is in itself exquisite joy. But in giving he cannot help bringing something to life in the other person, and this which is brought to life reflects back to him. . . . Giving implies to make the other person a giver also" (pp. 20–21).

Equally unrealistic, I suspect, is the new romanticism that holds up as an ideal the concept of "open" love in which the partner's sexual relationships with third parties is anticipated without anxiety or distress. I question whether most lovers can expect that they will be able to share sexual intimacy, particularly intercourse, with others without causing pain. I am not suggesting that extra-relational intercourse should be or necessarily will be destructive of love. On the contrary I think it is an evidence of the strength of love that it can transcend such a test. But love survives and often grows because it has the capacity to absorb the hurt, not because it is indifferent. Undoubtedly some people can enjoy deep relationships in which intercourse with others who are also loved is accepted freely. But this is uncommon. Studies of those living together or engaged in various forms of unconventional marriage show that anxiety about the involvement of the partner in other sexual relationships is often a major problem (Macklin, 1972; Olson, 1972; Constantine and Constantine, 1971). It is interesting to note that a recent example of a highly egalitarian marriage contract published in *Ms* (June, 1973) providing for a complete sharing of privileges and duties between man and wife, and for great independence in social life and careers, includes this clause: "The parties freely acknowledge their insecurity about sexual relationships beyond the partnership. Therefore the parties agree to maintain sexual fidelity to each other."

What we are talking about is not the possessiveness of the romantic lover who is terrified of losing the idealized other because he or she embodies all worth. We are not talking about the lack of trust in the beloved which is suspicious or fearful of any relationship with a member of the other sex. The jealousy which springs from such anxieties is inconsistent with love. It is also deeply rooted in the false identification of sex and coitus in our culture, which assumes that when a married person develops any depth of relationship with a third party of the other sex such a relationship is inevitably bound to lead to bed. A rediscovery of sexuality will help us to enjoy many such relationships and to recognize them as sexual, without any threat to the special union of the primary love consummated in intercourse.

What I am suggesting is that love needs to be able to assume that the supreme intimacy will not be shared with others. This is not destructive jealousy but the expectation of fidelity, the necessary trust in consistency and commitment without which love is diminished. Arieti (1972) asks the question: "Why can't a man love his wife and have relations with other women? He could indeed, but to the extent that he does that, his love is not liable to grow: it either remains stagnant or is already declining. If a man succumbs to the seductive influence of another woman, he does not necessarily cease to love his wife; but certainly his love is undergoing an injury which may not be healed. Any strong experience such as mature sexuality, reaches the heights, or what Maslow called a peak experience, only if it is shared with the person one loves. To know that the loved one had attempted to have a peak experience with somebody else is difficult to endure. Love, like freedom, is something which has to be safeguarded, not taken for granted: it requires a sustained effort, a commitment" (p. 64).

That last word "commitment" is a perennial source of misunderstanding between the generations. Few students will question the general premise that love involves some commitment to the beloved, concern for his or her future, obligations which cannot be lightly repudiated. Fromm's *The Art of Loving* (1956) is a popular book on campus, and he emphasizes that "love should be essentially an act of will, of decision to commit my life completely to that of one other person. . . . To love somebody is not just a strong feeling—it is a decision, it is a judgment, it is a promise" (p. 47). Most will agree with Mayeroff's (1971) statement: "Devotion is essential to caring, just as it is an integral part of friendship. I commit myself to the other and to a largely unforseeable future" (p. 8). But the adult world maintains that sexual love involves a lifelong obligation formally expressed in marriage, and most people under thirty find such a conclusion unnecessary.

Vincent (1973) points out that there is a major value revolution in progress: "One thematic thread permeating recent changes in attitudes in many areas of life (sexual, economic, political, social reform, and health services) is the emphasis on 'here and now.' This emphasis is not unique to couples' attitude of 'why wait?' for premarital or extramarital coital experience. It is part and parcel of a broader theme, *the impatience with patience.*" The generation gap is vividly reflected in a personal ad in *The Village Voice*: "Davis—One year is a long time. Let's make us last forever. Happy Anniversary. I love you. Adele."

The adult world regards a year's partnership as a mere beginning and assumes that it is planned for life. Many students, however much they may hope it will "last forever," see a formal, lifelong commitment as hypocritical, outmoded and premature. Hypocritical, because they know that the average marriage only lasts seven years. Outmoded, because it is historically linked to the assumption of early parenthood which can now be avoided by contraception. Premature, because it forces people into perma-

nent bonds before they are ready for them and leads to unnecessary tragedy—not only for them but for any children
they may have before they discover their mistake. The idea
of commitment to each other does not mean, for many, the
assumption that commitment must be lifelong. While
there may be the hope and even the expectation that a profound relationship will prove to have the quality of permanence, the idea of giving love a legal form, of institu-
tionalizing it in a public ceremony, is to many people
superfluous. One student who was sleeping with a man she
loved and "couldn't think of sleeping with anyone else"
made it clear that they had no intention of getting married in the near future. Both had individual plans for for-
eign travel. She *hoped* she would be with her present boyfriend when they were ready to have children and marry,
but she concluded: "Planning the future too carefully is
foolish for we may be dead tomorrow" (Smith, 1972).

I find myself greatly in sympathy with students who hes-
itate to make a lifelong commitment and I believe that if
marriage is to fulfill a real need in human life it must undergo significant changes.* But it is a great oversimplification to suppose that love is inconsistent with marital
commitment, obligation and even duty. One writer asks,
"How can marriage be fulfilling to mates or children when
it is maintained by legal fiat, not by the desires of the partners to the relationship?" (Greenwald, 1970). Of course
it cannot if the "legal fiat" is an externally imposed obligation. But marriage is not that: it is a commitment freely
entered into, the act of love once undertaken and still significant. There may come a time, alas, when that decision
has lost all meaning and love has died: then the legal bond
should be terminated. But in many people's experience

* Some of these are discussed in Chapter IX.

the tension between love's past commitment and love's present growth or survival is not a contradiction but a creative challenge.

Many marriages survive and grow *because of* rather than in spite of the public commitment and the relative difficulty of separation. Despite the common assertion "I wouldn't want to stay together simply because we had to" there are many situations in which love is sustained and eventually deepened simply because the marriage cannot be terminated at will. Many people find that they only discover what love is really about when they have experienced the kind of crisis that would have led to the breakup of any private arrangement. Cuber and Harroff (1966) quote one man as saying: "My wife and I came close—well, maybe not quite 'close'—to divorce a few years ago. But we stuck it out. Later we grew up, I guess. Anyway, we are now genuinely in love; the old bickering and even the cheating are gone. If we hadn't just refused to take the easy, thoughtless, narrowly selfish way out, where would we be now? Alone—or married to someone else and in the same fix. We'd be guilty—bitter probably" (p. 21).

Sex between married people has its own dangers—indifference, boredom, repetition. But, contrary to popular opinion among the unmarried, sex does not necessarily lose its flavor in marriage. A poll of college graduates found that 34 percent said sex was just as satisfying in the later as in the earlier years of marriage, and 24 percent said it was more enjoyable (*The Saturday Evening Post*, December 31, 1966). An extensive study of married women found that more than 50 percent rated the sexual satisfaction of their marriages "very good" (Bell and Bell, 1972). And marital sex has one advantage: a husband and wife do not need to demonstrate prowess, worth or skill, in fear of losing the other. They are free (if they will) to grow together without needing continual reassurance that they should stay together. Here is one woman's analysis: "Without marrying I had lots of intimate long-term relationships, but I never really committed myself. Now I find after marriage that I couldn't have accomplished growth any other way. There is growth in marriage in terms of taking on something, and casting off something. Growth is a process, something you have to enter into. What was it I left behind? . . . I suppose I left behind my own shell, and took on the ability to open up myself. That is commitment, to completely open up to another" (O'Neill and O'Neill, 1972, pp. 26–27).

To talk about "trial marriage" or to imagine that living together (however valuable an experience at the right time) is the same experience as marriage is nonsense. You can no more have a trial marriage than you can have a trial baby. The fact that no public or legal steps have been taken to assume full responsibility for each other makes a vast difference. It's the finality and irreversibility of the commitment of marriage that constitutes its significance and its potential value. But it also constitutes its potential cost. Divorce does not reverse or undo marriage, it merely terminates it. The experience remains part of the permanent history of both persons involved. To be somebody's ex-husband or ex-wife is still to be related to them in a special way. That's a good reason for postponing it until you are as sure as you can be of success—and that means until you have come to terms with yourself as a sexual being and learned to relate sexually with some maturity to others.

CHAPTER VII

Gay Can Be Good

Homosexuality is perhaps the aspect of sex about which our society remains most ambivalent. Despite the recommendation of the American Law Institute almost twenty years ago that private homosexual acts between consenting adults should be excluded from the criminal law, only nine states (not including the two most populous, New York and California) legally permit homosexual practices. Despite the long struggle of the Mattachine Society (of whose Board of Advisors this author is a member) and the more recent protests of the Gay Liberation movement, homosexuals are the object of widespread discrimination. They are open to harrassment, intimidation, assault, public ridicule, legal prosecution, entrapment, blackmail and denial of employment or housing *simply* because of their sexual preference. "To be a homosexual in our society," says Dennis Altman (1971) "is to be constantly aware that one bears a stigma. . . . Like most gay people, I know myself to be part of a minority feared, disliked and persecuted by the majority" (p. 13). Although homosexuals and lesbians are often treated with sensitivity in newspapers and magazines and on the stage and screen (notably in *Sunday, Bloody Sunday* and in *Two English Girls*; less notably in the more popular

Boys in the Band *) there is still a high level of what Wein-berg (1972) calls "homophobia" among those over thirty. Although more college students now accept homosexuality as a viable alternative life style, a Kinsey Institute study reported in 1973 that 79 percent of the adult population disapprove of homosexual relations even in the context of love. Nevertheless we can identify a number of respects in which our culture has modified or is in process of modifying its attitude, and these do represent significant change for the better.

We no longer identify homosexuality with homosexual acts. It was long assumed that anyone who engaged in sexual intimacy with a member of the same sex was ex-hibiting a fundamental, identifiable homosexual nature. Not a few men and women have suffered untold anxiety and guilt because they have been involved at high school or college in some homosexual activity or relationship and have then been assumed by their peers, their parents and themselves to be a "pervert." By a peculiar logic the condi-tion is assumed to be *both* the consequence of individual choice (hence blameworthy) *and* inherent (hence perma-nent and unalterable rather than a temporary phase of adolescence).

Kinsey (1948) found that whereas approximately one out of every three males had homosexual experience during or after adolescence, only one out of every twenty or twenty-five was committed to homosexual relationships in adult-hood (Gagnon and Simon, 1968). He argued therefore that we should avoid using the term *homosexual* as a noun, and

---

* The comment "Show me a happy homosexual and I'll show you a gay corpse" is understandably resented by many homosexuals. But Karlen (1971) found a surprising number of those he interviewed felt it reflected the truth.

should speak only of individuals with varying amounts of homosexual experience. This may be a counsel of perfection, but we can at least reserve the nouns homosexual or lesbian* for men or women who *in adulthood prefer to achieve sexual gratification with a member of the same sex.* Homosexual attraction is often a passing phase of sexual development, and many men and women who are aroused to the point of orgasm in homosexual encounters are not in fact homosexuals. While most of those who are (in the strict sense) homosexuals are probably aware of the fact by their twenties (and some much earlier), some who suspect or fear that they are homosexuals at college eventually discover that they are not (West, 1960). A task force of the National Institute for Mental Health, reporting in 1969 (McCaffrey, 1972, p. 152), expressed the opinion that "perhaps fifty percent of predominantly homosexual persons having some homosexual orientation and who present themselves for treatment can be helped to become predominantly heterosexual." *

* The word *homosexual* is derived from the Greek word meaning *same,* not from the Latin for *man,* and refers to males and females. The term *lesbian* (from the Greek island of Lesbos, home of the poetess Sappho) is used for female homosexuals. It is generally estimated that about 5 percent of the population of the United States are homosexual.

Contrary to popular mythology homosexuals are not identifiable by external physical or behavioral characteristics. Very few homosexuals are transvestites ("cross-dressers") or concerned to mimic the other sex. The male "queen" and the female "butch" are in no way typical; a male homosexual may be thoroughly muscular in appearance and a lesbian entirely "feminine" in manner or dress.

* The qualification "who present themselves" is important. The voluntary interest of the person in seeking help is of primary importance. A college health clinic or counseling service will often provide or recommend the appropriate resources. Information about agencies and professionals throughout the country with particular qualifications to advise on homosexual questions can be obtained from:

A great deal of misunderstanding arises from the popular misuse of the term *latent homosexual*. Frequently it is wrongly employed to imply that anyone who has homosexual inclinations at any time is basically a homosexual. When someone engages in homosexual contact in circumstances (such as in a single-sex school or during service in the armed forces) where all heterosexual outlets are unavailable he or she may be called a latent homosexual with the suggestion that the real nature of the individual's sexual orientation has now been exposed. But most of these people will revert to heterosexuality when normal opportunities recur: they never were really homosexuals. If used at all the term *latent homosexual* should be reserved for those who in adulthood prefer sexual experience with a member of the same sex but who—perhaps because of deep religious prohibitions or strong social pressures—do not give expression to their desires. Some people in this category are not able to acknowledge their homosexuality honestly even to themselves. They may be among the most vehement in their condemnation of overt homosexuals because they are repudiating in others what they most fear and (because of continuing social prejudice) despise in themselves.

We no longer think that homosexuality is a threat to our social structure. It is recognized today that the long-standing fear that homosexuals are a danger to children is nonsense: heterosexuals are just as likely to molest the young.

The Institute for the Study of Human Resources, 2256 Venice Boulevard, Suite 203, Los Angeles, Ca. 90006 (telephone 213:735-4357)

The Homosexual Community Counseling Center, 921 Madison Avenue, New York, N.Y. 10021 (telephone 212:988-7632)

The Center for Special Problems, 2107 Van Ness Avenue, San Francisco, Ca. 94109 (telephone 415:558-4801)

The numbers involved in a recent report of homosexual mass murder are small compared to the number of women raped and killed annually by heterosexuals. The "prairie fire" view of homosexuality, which supposes that if the possibility of sexual pleasure with one's own sex becomes widely known it will spread apace and eliminate heterosexuality, is still held, but it fails entirely to recognize the facts. The social pressures towards heterosexuality are so strong in our culture that only those whose orientation is firmly homosexual are likely to accept the embarrassment, shame and humiliation involved in deviance from the societal norm.

A few heterosexual men and women, perhaps as a result of being discovered in some homosexual relationship and wrongly labeled by others and themselves as "perverts," may find temporary security and acceptance in the homosexual milieu. Many others will for a time engage in bisexual behavior in the course of clarifying their basic sexual identity and emotional commitment. But the fundamental evolutionary reproductive drive guarantees that most people will prefer the other sex, and homosexual behavior, which has existed openly in other societies, has never permanently satisfied more than a small minority. The roots of true homosexuality lie far below the level of simple choice: nobody makes up his or her mind to *be* a homosexual, though someone may choose whether or not to engage in homosexual acts or to accept the fact of being homosexual. Altman (1971) thinks "there is at least sometimes an element of deliberate choice in the adoption of homosexuality" since it represents a rebellion against the norm of marriage/family/home (p. 18).

More adequate information about all types of sexuality is more likely to lead to a reduction in the number of people suffering unnecessarily because of confusion about their sexual identity. If men and women know that some homosexual attraction is common among heterosexuals, they are less likely to be disturbed when they discover a homosexual element in themselves. If they are liberated from a sense of obligation to play stereotyped sex roles they will not fear that deviation from the expectations of the peer group necessarily implies homosexuality. Men with less than average interest in sexual adventure on campus will cease to be haunted by anxieties about their masculinity. Women who become deeply involved in Women's Lib and find themselves exclusively intimate with members of their own sex will not be misled into supposing that they are necessarily lesbians.

Far from being a threat to society, homosexuals have in fact contributed greatly to our culture. It is necessary only to mention the names of Leonardo, Michelangelo, Tchaikovsky, Whitman, Gide and Proust—though the point should not be exaggerated since several of the more notorious kings of England were also homosexuals (West, 1960). Their capacity to be integrated, constructive members of the community can be increased only as they are freed of discrimination, contempt and fear of blackmail or persecution. In the long run Gay Liberation is working for the best interests of heterosexuals as well as homosexuals by giving homosexuals a sense of worth and enabling them to take their place as acceptable members of society.

We recognize that homosexual acts are not necessarily degrading. Any sexual act *can* be degrading if it involves the debasement of another human being; intercourse can be degrading even in marriage. For many people there is something unattractive about observing or even imagining the sexual intimacies of others; we find it hard to conceive how physical acts that have never been expressions of love or affection for us can be so for others. As Havelock Ellis (1933) remarked, "Not even the most recognized methods of sexual intercourse can well be described as 'aesthetic.' It is not understood that here, amid the most intimate mysteries of love, we are in a region where the cold and abstract viewpoints either of science or of aesthetics are out of place unless qualified by more specially human emotions" (p. 295).

Homosexuals enjoy sexual pleasure by all the means available to heterosexuals—other than by inserting the penis in the vagina. They engage in kissing, caressing, petting to orgasm, cunnilingus (kissing or licking the labia minora and clitoris), fellatio (kissing or sucking the penis and scrotum) and sometimes (in the case of males) in anal intercourse. Oral sex, although long unacceptable and still strictly illegal in many states, even between man and wife, is common among educated heterosexuals. In 1965 a study of a relatively conservative group of college students found that two-thirds of the men and half of the women had oral-genital sexual experience (Robinson et al., 1972). Anal intercourse (technically called "sodomy" in the United States and "buggery" in Britain) is less common among heterosexuals, but the practice is enthusiastically endorsed by the author of the widely read guide *The Sensuous Woman*. Emotional abhorrence about homosexual practices is therefore inappropriate and steadily decreasing among heterosexuals. Where it persists it may be due to a mistaken assumption that, because oral or anal sex are common between homosexuals, these acts in themselves express or lead to homosexuality. But this is not the case. They are only homosexual acts when those engaging in them desire a partner of the same sex.

Even the rigid religious condemnation of homosexuality

has been modified. The Judaeo-Christian tradition has been obsessed by what has been called "the Sodom and Gomorrah complex," based on the Old Testament story (Genesis 19) in which these two cities were supposedly destroyed with fire and brimstone for moral perversity. But this interpretation dates only from New Testament times, and recently scholars have questioned whether the sin so dramatically condemned was homosexuality at all. Most religious authorities would now agree that "it is no longer possible to maintain the belief that homosexual practices were once punished by a Divine judgment upon their perpetrators so terrible and conclusive as to preclude any subsequent discussion of the question." Still less can it be held that "an act of God has determined once and for all what attitude Church and State ought to adopt towards the problem of sexual inversion" (Bailey, 1955, p. 28).

In the past decade there has been a remarkable move towards a humane and positive understanding of homosexuality in Christian circles. A report issued in England by a group of Friends made this significant statement:

Surely it is the nature and quality of a relationship that matters: one must not judge it by its outward appearance but by its inner worth. Homosexual affection can be as selfless as heterosexual affection, and therefore we cannot see that it is in some way morally worse. Homosexual affection may of course be an emotion which some find aesthetically disgusting, but one cannot base Christian morality on a capacity for such disgust. Neither are we happy with the thought that all homosexual behaviour is sinful: motive and circumstances degrade or ennoble any act (Heron, 1963, p. 36).

Since then homosexuals have been ordained in several churches, congregations for homosexuals have been established in a number of cities and a considerable body of literature has been produced with the intention of developing a religious ethic for homosexuality. In his introduction to the best of these books, *Is Gay Good?* (Oberholtzer, 1971), Joseph Fletcher writes: "It seems to me that there is no ethical objection to homosexuality as such, even though some of us have aesthetic objections of a personal order. There is, I would hold, nothing intrinsically good or evil per se in any sexual act. Whether it is right or wrong depends on its situation, and what is sometimes right is other times wrong. Homosexual acts can be morally objectionable in some situations, in exactly the same way that heterosexual acts can be" (p. 10).

Official religious bodies have, inevitably, been much slower to come to terms with the new understanding of the dynamics of homosexuality. It should be noted, however, that the adoption in Britain in 1967 of the proposals of the Wolfenden Report legalizing homosexual acts between consenting adults was supported by both the Church of England and the Roman Catholic Church. And the journal *Commonweal* in an editorial in April, 1973, stated: "Recently, some Catholic moralists have . . . cautiously agreed in the professional journals that under certain conditions, which may differ with each individual, a Catholic homosexual can enter an active homosexual relationship and still receive the sacraments and live a life of sexual love which does not necessarily separate him from the love of God." Cautious and qualified it may be, but such a statement would have been quite unthinkable ten years ago.

It is no longer assumed that all homosexuals are emotionally sick. Many psychiatrists and psychologists do hold that homosexuals are ill simply in virtue of their sexual bias—on the grounds that they have been unable to develop according to the biological and cultural norm of heterosexuality. The most respected contemporary proponent of this view is Irving Bieber (1962), who came to the conclusion that homosexuality is the result of "hidden but incapacitating fears of the opposite sex," a pathological condition symptomatic of "fear and inhibition of heterosexual expression." * But others argue that pyschotherapists see only those homosexuals who are emotionally disturbed for one reason or another, and that the great majority of homosexuals are at least as able as most heterosexuals to cope with the demands of life without mental breakdown. The social, religious and personal opprobrium under which homosexuals have suffered for so long may be a major factor in causing their emotional problems, not the homosexuality itself. It is interesting that lesbians, who have always been less persecuted for their sexual behavior than male homosexuals, present themselves much less frequently for psychiatric treatment (Robertiello, 1973).

Regular personality tests applied to homosexuals have been found to show the same range of patterns as those of heterosexuals (Hooker, 1956, 1965). A task force of the National Institute of Mental Health reported in 1969 that "homosexual individuals vary widely in terms of their emotional and social adjustments. Some persons who engage in homosexual behavior function well in everyday life; others are severely maladjusted or disturbed in their functioning. There are those whose total life is dominated by homosexual impulses and those whose sexual behavior

---

* The theory is far from new. Bieber's work was significant because he and his colleagues compared a large number of (106) homosexual patients with a control group of (100) heterosexuals, and claimed to have established definitive conclusions from the statistical evidence. The claim has been hotly contested.

is just one component in their total life experience" (Mc-Caffrey, 1972, p. 146). In 1970 the Executive Committee of the National Institute of Mental Health approved the statement that homosexual behavior "does not constitute a specific mental or emotional illness." In December 1973 the Board of Trustees of the American Psychiatric Association unanimously agreed that homosexuality "by itself does not necessarily constitute a psychiatric disorder," although for some who are disturbed or in conflict over their sexuality it may involve "a sexual orientation disturbance" (*The New York Times,* December 16, 1973).

Interestingly enough Freud clearly denied that homosexuality constituted a neurotic illness. In his famous letter to the American mother of a homosexual, written in 1935, he said: "Homosexuality is assuredly no advantage, but it is nothing to be ashamed of, no vice, no degradation, it cannot be classified as an illness; we consider it to be a variation of the sexual function produced by a certain arrest of sexual development" (Ruitenbeek, 1963, p. 1). We may, perhaps, following the clue of Freud's last phrase, call homosexuality a form of sexual inadequacy. But to say that someone has failed (or has been prevented) from attaining optimum sexual self-realization is quite a different thing from saying that he or she is mentally or emotionally sick. All of us are inadequate to varying degrees in different aspects of our personalities and relationships. But inadequacies of one kind or another do not necessarily or usually prevent us from living reasonably happy, socially constructive lives, and many homosexuals are as integrated and mature as any heterosexuals.*

* Karlen (1971), who came to a similar conclusion on the basis of an extensive study, added this qualification: "However, I also feel that only a small minority of homosexuals reach the upper levels of adaptive success. And even if their homosexuality is 'encapsulated,' one must question

The area in which homosexuals seem to have particular difficulty is in integrating physical satisfaction and personal relationships. This is certainly not true of all homosexuals, many of whom (especially lesbians) do establish-long-standing, loving, truly personal unions (Hedblom, 1972). But male homosexuals often seem to prefer sexual contacts of an anonymous, purely genital type, and they not infrequently give the impression that they are only interested in orgasmic release with any partner who is physically attractive to them (Hyde, 1970; Humphreys, 1970). One man told Karlen (1971) that homosexuals will "do anything to get the guy they want, and you don't see many couples stick together for very long. You feel that in the atmosphere of most of the gay bars. I've learned to really despise those places, where people hang around and appraise each other like pieces of meat" (p. 158). Hoffman (1969), a sympathetic observer of the gay scene, comments: "What is striking about these acquaintanceships, and even about many of the love affairs that last for several weeks to several months, is their shallowness. These people use each other in an instrumental, narcissistic way to gratify their own fantasies" (p. 70).

We have to remember that social pressures force the male homosexual to avoid permanent relationships which might gain public notice. The ever-present threat of entrapment or blackmail discourages them from sharing even their names with sexual partners. And having been taught by society that his sexual inclinations are contemptible, the homosexual easily comes to view himself as dirty and unredeemable. He accepts the stigma "queer" and views his partners in the same way. At least, he did until

the value of encapsulating one's love life. Many well-adjusted homosexuals would probably be even better adjusted without their deviation" (p. 595). The last statement is obviously highly speculative.

recently. Perhaps the most important contribution that Gay Liberation is making is to enable homosexuals to gain the self-esteem and self-respect that the straight world has so long denied them.

As homosexuals erase the low self-image with which they have been imprinted, and as society begins to accept them as people (neither depraved nor sick) the possibility of serious, loving relationships is opened up. Humphreys (1972) notes that "on the overt side of the gay world, the virile influence of hip culture is having profound effects. . . . At least in word, if not always in deed, these overt leaders of the gay community espouse the deeper, more personal type of relationship. Theirs is a search for lovers, for men with whom they may build abiding relationships" (p. 77). The increasing number who want to enter into a permanent "marriage" is indicative of the change, and the readiness of some religious and secular authorities to recognize such unions is encouraging. It may be that once homosexual relationships have been fully accepted in our society a union of personal relationship and sexual intimacy will be much easier for the homosexual. But for the time-being it behooves us to remember that such a union is not by any means always achieved by those who do not have to struggle with the burden of society's oppression and misunderstanding.* Many heterosexuals are far from mature in their capacity to make their sexual behavior expressive of truly human caring and openness to their partners.

* It is also worth pointing out that Kinsey (1948) found that the number of sexual "outlets" enjoyed by homosexuals averaged one a week at the age of twenty-five, whereas the average married young heterosexual had intercourse every other day. Homosexuals are therefore in fact *less* sexually active than heterosexuals, even though they may be more likely (because of the absence of socially acceptable opportunities and/or permanent bonds) to be promiscuous.

We no longer talk about "curing" homosexuals. The possibility of cure implies first an illness and then a diagnosis. We have seen that homosexuality is not a specific illness, though many homosexuals, like many heterosexuals, are emotionally sick and (again, like many heterosexuals) their problem may be sexual in origin or manifestation. Nor is there any agreement as to a definable originating cause for homosexuality. The possibility that abnormalities of hormonal level may be a factor has been revived as a result of studies at the Masters' Reproductive Biology Foundation (reported in the *New England Journal of Medicine,* November 1971), and by the work of Money and Ehrhardt (1972); but few authorities regard the evidence as fully convincing, and the administration of testosterone to male homosexuals does not affect the *orientation* of their sexual drives.

A more generally accepted view is that homosexuals have been unable to establish a clear sense of personal sexual identity because of inadequate relationships and models within the family unit. Bieber (1962) found that a high percentage of homosexuals he studied had "close-binding-intimate" mothers and emotionally detached or hostile fathers. The fact that one of two children raised in the same family may grow up homosexual and the other heterosexual raises questions as to the adequacy of this theory, but as Magee (1969) points out, two children in the same family may have very different relationships to the parents and to siblings. A third possibility, which certainly seems to be an element in the history of many lesbians, is that early sexual experiences have led the individual to prefer a member of the same sex—perhaps because encounters with the other sex have been painful or embarrassing.

The summary of the complex situation given by Hooker

(1961) still stands: "From this writer's research on male homosexuality, it becomes increasingly clear that homosexuality is an extraordinarily complicated phenomenon, in which the causative factors are multiple. Many factors co-operate in producing it. Among these are: inappropriate identifications with the opposite-sexed parent; fear of hostility to either parent; reversal of masculine and feminine roles in parents; cultural overemphasis on the stereotype of 'masculinity,' which produces feelings of inadequacy in males who are not able to fulfil this expectation; rigid dichotomy of male and female social roles, with failure to allow for individuals who do not fit easily into either of these; and easier access to sexual gratification with members of one's own sex in adolescence, resulting in habit patterns which persist. This is by no means a complete list" (pp. 171–72).

Society as a whole, and psychiatrists in particular, have shown an obsessive concern to reverse homosexual behavior patterns. Weinberg (1972) describes some of the more inhumane attempts at desensitization: emetic persuasion, aversive conditioning and even brain surgery. He points out that there is something odd about the fact that those who use such methods often *do* regard homosexuals as sick, but apparently feel obliged to put pressure on their patients to undergo cures they do not really want. "We expect despair and hair-pulling when someone close to us is desperately ill. But why this assault? One does not assault someone merely because he is ill. One assaults him because one is mortally afraid of him" (p. 4). And this fear, Weinberg suggests, is due in part to the fact that the homosexual fails to conform to the social pattern of marriage and parenthood, and in part to a sexist contempt for the male who "acts like a woman." *

* This would explain why lesbianism arouses a far less violent reaction. There are reasons to think that religious condemnation of homosexuality

There is a growing body of opinion, even among those who regard homosexuality as a sickness (e.g., Hatterer, 1973), that it is better for a person who is exclusively homosexual in adulthood to be counseled to accept the fact, and to develop self-confidence and self-respect as a homosexual, rather than encouraging questions and conflicts or persisting in attempts at treatment. "The elimination of homosexual behavior should not be the central focus of effective psychotherapy. The choice of continuing or abandoning such behavior should be left to the patient to be made after he has a real cognitive awareness of the factors that produced his sexual pattern. The primary object is to free the patient from the tyranny of his own unconscious so that he is able to make a rational choice and to continue in human relationships characterized by fidelity and the ability to receive and give love and care regardless of the gender of his partner. Fidelity and the ability to receive and give love and care are the hallmarks of emotional maturity and human strength; they are stark necessities for individual development and social evolution. The strength of our society seems to be dependent on how many citizens find their respective identities, fuse them in love and cooperative consideration, and create. Whether this creation involves procreation is a moot point. But certainly productivity cannot be in question as an essential quality of adult fulfillment, and it should be our principal aim as therapists to help the homosexual implement and integrate his productive potential with that of his society" (Willis, 1967a, p. 24).

It is a central theme of this book that what matters about sexuality is its integration with human relationships

sprang from outrage at the affront it represented to the dignity of the male in early patriarchal society (Bruns, 1967).

which are caring, responsible, honest and loving. It is greatly to be wished that in our society these criteria will eventually be accepted—rather than those of sexual orientation or marital status. I know homosexuals whose fidelity, sensitivity and integrity equal or surpass that of most of the heterosexuals I know: yet the majority of our society absurdly condemns them as immoral just because they differ in loving a member of the same sex.

As this tragically unfair and inhumane attitude gives way to understanding and respect (as it must) the anxiety about whether one is or is not homosexual will eventually disappear. People will be able to accept the fact that it doesn't really matter all that much whether or not they are homosexual, but that it does matter whether their sexual relations with others are mature and creative. Both heterosexuals and homosexuals will be set free from a compulsive need to demonstrate *what* they are and able to concern themselves with *how* they are as sexual beings.

CHAPTER VIII

Sexual Liberation

This is not a chapter on the political and social dimensions of Women's Liberation, which would require another book. I do affirm my support for every effort to obtain full equality for women in every sphere, to put an end to the legal and economic discrimination under which they still suffer and to ensure the passage and effective implementation of the Equal Rights Amendment. But we are here concerned with the narrower question of the new understanding of female sexuality, which has paralleled and to some extent strengthened the wider movement.

We now know that femininity is biologically more fundamental than masculinity. In the embryological development of the human sexual apparatus the basic tissue is female, and unless the masculinizing hormone (testosterone) interferes with the process, feminine reproductive organs develop. "Strictly speaking, we can no longer refer to the 'undifferentiated' or 'bisexual' phase of initial embryonic existence. The early embryo is not undifferentiated: 'it' is a female. In the beginning, we were all created females; and if this were not so, we would not be here at all" (Sherfey, 1972, p. 38). Instead of speaking, as we do, of the clitoris as a "small penis" we should, Sherfey sug-

155

gests, speak of the penis as an "exaggerated clitoris" (p. 46).

We also know, as a result of the researches of Masters and Johnson (1966) that women are not only able to experience sexual pleasure as intense and as satisfying as that of men, but that many women can maintain orgasmic experience longer, and reach several climaxes in rapid succession.* Sherfey points out that physiologically a woman could go on having orgasms indefinitely if sheer exhaustion did not intervene—though she notes that a woman sometimes may be emotionally satisfied to the full in the absence of *any* orgasmic expression.

Equally important is the final exposé by Masters and Johnson (1966) of the Freudian myth of the vaginal orgasm. Freud, and many of his disciples, believed that the female was capable of two distinct types of orgasm. The masturbatory or clitoral orgasm was characteristic of childhood. During normal adolescence the erotic focus was transferred from the clitoris to the vagina: the significance was that the vagina is the organ of reproduction, and sexual maturity was therefore associated with the woman's role as a potential mother. Incidentally it implied that her sexual and human potential was only realized when she had the help of the male penis to bring about vaginal orgasm. Not only did the theory lead to untold anxieties and guilt among women who failed to achieve the transfer, but any form of female self-arousal was regarded as immature and even perverse.

We now know that the *physiological* process of orgasm is identical for the female, whether produced by masturba-

---

* A major thesis of this book is that sexuality, both male and female, is distorted when orgasmic "achievement" is seen as the goal of all sexual contact. However, since traditionally female sexuality has been defined in terms of primarily non-orgasmic activity, the recognition of female orgasmic capacity represents a significant social change—even though its significance as an isolated fact can be exaggerated.

tion, petting or intercourse. Even if there is no penetration, the lower third of the vagina contracts rhythmically during orgasm. If intercourse takes place and orgasm is experienced with penile intromission it is the friction of the penis on the labia minora and indirectly on the clitoris that is the immediate physical cause. Thus *biologically* there is no distinction between vaginal and clitoral orgasm.

This does not mean that it may not make a difference to a woman whether she has intercourse or not. The lower third of the vagina is erotogenic and the thrusting of the penis does add to the woman's pleasure. While orgasm in masturbation or petting is often enjoyed more quickly and with greater intensity, orgasm during intercourse is often reported to be more satisfying and to be felt as emanating from the vagina (Masters and Johnson, 1966; Robertiello, 1970; Clark, 1970; Singer and Singer, 1972). One of Schaefer's subjects described the difference thus: "A vaginal orgasm is more of a full pelvic feeling. It's not localized. It's like the difference between having your pelvis on fire and just having a clitoral bonfire going" (p. 139). Another woman told her: "When I could only have a clitoral orgasm with some manipulation, it made me feel as though I were participating in something unilaterally. It's as though I'm on the receiving end exclusively at that time. In a vaginal orgasm I feel very much as though I am participating with somebody" (p. 140).

In this limited sense, then, the phrase "vaginal orgasm" does have a valid meaning. But we must avoid making it, as Freudian orthodoxy has done, a criterion of psychological or sexual maturity (Sherfey, 1972; Bardwick, 1971; Levin et al., 1972). Some women of obvious emotional and sexual maturity are never able to enjoy orgasm except with some manual or oral stimulation of the clitoral area.*

* The term clitoral area is used rather than clitoris because (1) the

Many others need considerable experience and patient manual or oral stimulation before they can have an orgasm during intercourse.* The significant thing is that women no longer need feel that they are psychological cripples if they enjoy sexual pleasure in masturbation or in relationships with other women. Seaman quotes the following from a prominent feminist: "I think it's wonderful that women have discovered masturbation, because it will enable us to keep apart from men as long as necessary. . . . Some of the women I know are so pathetic. They run around looking for a man, any man at all, just because they don't know how to masturbate" (p. 69).

The important question arises: is this new understanding of female sexuality likely to result in a radical change in the relationships between the sexes? Are the traditional differences in attitude towards sexuality likely to disappear? Are men and women so alike except in their biological and physical structures that changes in culture and gender roles can be expected to put an end to any distinctively "feminine" character or temperament? It had been widely assumed that feminine sexuality is more deeply integrated with the whole person, more diffuse than specifically genital, less easily aroused by impersonal stimuli and more dependent on interpersonal relationships for meaning and value. The psychoanalyst Karen Horney (1927), for example, in affirming the positive elements in female sexuality against Freud, claimed that whereas men are able

---

clitoris itself is often too sensitive for direct stimulation and arousal is best achieved by massaging the mons veneris and labia minora on either side of the clitoris, and (2) just before climax the clitoris withdraws under its "hood" and direct contact with it is impossible (Masters and Johnson, 1966).

* In Seaman's study (1972) this was true of very nearly half the women she questioned.

with relative ease to dissociate emotional and sensual love, in women "the emotional life is, as a rule, much more closely and uniformly connected with sexuality," so that "she cannot give herself completely when she does not love or is not loved" (p. 89). And in rejoinder to Freud's assertion that women were merely incomplete, castrated men, she exclaimed, "At this point, I, as a woman, ask in amazement, and what about motherhood? And the blissful consciousness of bearing a new life within oneself? And the ineffable happiness of the increasing expectation of the appearance of this new being? And the joy when it finally makes its appearance and one holds it for the first time in one's arms? And the deep pleasurable feeling of satisfaction in suckling it and the happiness of the whole period when the infant needs her care?" (Horney, 1926, p. 60).

Erikson (1963), on the basis of extensive observation of children, claimed that there exists a fundamental difference (corresponding to the physical capacity to be an inseminator or a child-bearer) between the way boys and girls respond to space. In playing with bricks, he observed, boys build upward and outward, whereas girls construct enclosed spaces: the one sex expresses its fundamental biological and psychological makeup in erecting, constructing and elaborating, whereas the other is concerned to include, enclose and hold safely. But such characteristics are dismissed as purely cultural by authors like Millett (1971), who claims that the sexes are "inherently in everything alike, save reproductive systems, secondary sexual characteristics, orgasmic capacity, and genetic and morphological structure" (p. 93) * and rejects the idea of "inner space"

* In view of modern knowledge of the inseparability of the physical, mental and emotional, this seems inherently improbable. Mead (1949) asks pertinently, "Out of bodies fashioned for complementary rôles in perpetuating the race, what differences in functioning, in capacities, in

and motherhood as a male myth intended to impose domestic serfdom on women.

There can be little question that gender roles are to a great extent dictated by cultural factors. Margaret Mead in her well-known study *Sex and Temperament in Three Primitive Societies* (1935) vividly illustrates the diversity of male and female functions in three New Guinea tribes: the Arapesh, whose men are gentle and maternal, and share the nurturing roles of the women; the Mundugumor, whose men and women both are aggressive and insensitive; and the Tchambuli, whose women do the serious work while the men devote themselves to ceremonial dancing and art.

But this variety and the obvious deviations from what we tend to think of as the "norm" of male and female roles do not necessarily lead to the conclusion that *all* psychological distinctions are culturally derived. Virtually all known societies invest women with a greater responsibility for the nurturing of children (Packard, 1968). Mead (1949) found that, despite the exceptions she describes, certain attitudes and capacities generally distinguish the two sexes: men tend to be more constructive and exploratory, and women to be more empathetic and supportive. For example, although the Arapesh give full reign to the nurturing capacities of the male, it is still the men who (reluctantly) perform the functions of leadership in the community. In the Mundugumor society women are markedly aggressive and weak in maternal instincts; but the result is a society

---

sensitivities, in vulnerabilities, arise? How is what men can do related to the fact that their reproductive rôle is over in a single act, what women can do related to the fact that their reproductive rôle takes nine months of gestation, and until recently many months of breast-feeding?" (pp. 56–57).

in which healthy, loving relationships are notably lacking, and in which sexual encounters have all the marks of immaturity—possessiveness, promiscuity and sadism. The Tchambuli males exhibit many so-called feminine traits, but they are really aggressive caricatures of what most of use regard as unattractive and non-essential in women—gossiping, bickering and competitive self-adornment.

In the final analysis only history can settle the question whether nature or nurture determines human sexual behavior. Most authorities seem inclined nowadays to attribute the differences between the sexes to a combination of the two. They recognize some innate male and female traits, differing in balance in each individual, but stress that cultural pressures and expectations can override these inherent distinctions. Stoller found that some children, born with the external genitalia of one sex and brought up by their parents in that role, persistently maintained that they belonged in fact to the other sex and were later found to exhibit the secondary characteristics of that other sex (Stoller, 1968). His somewhat reluctant conclusion was that, while postnatal forces are the major factor in establishing gender role, there does exist a biological force which is capable of sustaining a sense of masculinity or femininity in the face of all social and cultural pressures to the contrary.

The possibility that male and female characteristics are in part traceable to differences in nervous organization was suggested by Kinsey as long ago as 1948. In 1965 Young, Goy and Phoenix presented evidence that hormones, particularly during the prenatal period, have an effect on the central nervous system which in turn results in distinctive sexual behavior. In 1972 Money and Ehrhardt published the most thorough study of the subject yet attempted, *Man* *and Woman: Boy and Girl.** They found that post-natal cultural influences are of major importance in establishing behavior patterns. A boy who is brought up as a girl (because of some malformation of, or accident to, the external genitals) will probably develop the interests and attitudes characteristic of a girl. So gender identity is not pre-ordained by prenatal hormonal factors.

But on the other hand, according to Money and Ehrhardt, "it is premature to attribute all aspects of gender-identity to the post-natal period" (p. 18). Hormones acting on the unborn fetus "account not only for the shape of the external genitals but also for certain patterns of organization in the brain, especially, by inference, in the hypothalamic pathways that will subsequently influence certain aspects of sexual behavior . . . which are traditionally and culturally classified as predominantly boyish or girlish" (pp. 2–4). For example, girls who were subjected to the masculinizing hormone at a particular stage of embryonic development, manifest traditionally "boyish" behavior in adolescence. They play games with and compete with boys rather than with girls, prefer functional clothing to dresses, show little interest in small children, subordinate romance and marriage to career achievement and respond to erotic material in a masculine way. This does not mean that they are lesbians, or uninterested eventually in heterosexual partnerships; the difference is that their approach to people and their attitude to all human relationships (including

---

* In earlier studies Money had left the impression that he regarded gender roles as determined purely by post-natal influences, though in an interview with Karlen (1971) he denied that he had ever intended to be "so simpleminded." Hutt (1972) has drawn attention to some questionable deductions from the evidence in the earlier work, but she notes that by 1968 Money had acknowledged the possible effects of fetal hormones on psychosexual development—a position that is clearly affirmed in his work with Ehrhardt quoted here.

the sexual) is distinguishable in its emphasis from that of most girls. The conclusion seems to be unavoidable that hormonal factors operative before birth establish a presumptive pattern of behavior which is (in varying degrees) male or female. The post-natal influences of culture normally support and give specificity to this inherent tendency; but in some cases one factor and in some cases the other will predominate.*

Studies of infants conducted before cultural forces could have any significant effect on their self-image or expected roles appear to show marked differences between the way baby boys and baby girls react to their environment. Girls react more quickly to touch and pain and (unlike boys) gaze longer at photographs of faces than at geometric figures. They stop sucking a bottle if someone enters the room, whereas boys pay no attention to interruption. When frightened, year-old girls move towards their mothers while boys take up some other activity. If animals are raised in isolation and then put in a room with the young of their species the females rather than the males go to the infants and take care of them. Harlow (1965) observed marked differences in the behavior of male and female rhesus monkeys raised with inanimate surrogate "mothers" made of cloth which could not possibly have transmitted

* The possibility must be considered that certain characteristics we now identify as "feminine" gained that association because they were evolutionarily adaptive for women at the dawn of human society. It has been suggested that those women who were submissive, maternal and sexually restrained gained the protection of males, and therefore survived to bring children to maturity and contribute to the genetic pool. The more adventurous women who continued to compete with men in hunting would then have been "weeded out." The result would be the breeding into the female of the species, over hundreds of generations, of "innate" qualities of domestication and dependence (Tiger, 1969; Gadpaille, 1973). To what extent such characteristics could be easily modified by education or new social alignments is not clear.

"cultural" expectations. Males were markedly more threatening and more likely to initiate rough and tumble play, whereas females engaged in more grooming activities.

Such evidence is not conclusive, since there may be subtle ways in which human adults influence infants at or before birth. It has been suggested, for example, that parents handle children differently—treating new-born girls with more tenderness than boys. But as Professor Jerome Kagan of Harvard has argued, the earlier a particular difference appears the more likely it is to be due to biological rather than cultural factors, and the evidence "forces us to consider the possibility that some of the psychological differences between men and women may not be the product of experience alone but of subtle biological differences." Kagan recognizes that it is possible that the differences can be overcome but he suggests "we must ask if such a society will be satisfying to its members" once the complementarity of male and female attitudes and characters have been replaced by identity (*Time,* March 20, 1972).

*   *   *

I am wholeheartedly in favor of breaking down the stereotypes of male dominance and female passivity, and of radically modifying the gender roles that men and women have played for untold generations. But I am convinced that our understanding and enjoyment of sexuality will be more complete and humane if the special insights of women are respected and shared by *both* sexes rather than eliminated. The Katz study (1968) came to this conclusion:

The percentage of women for whom sex and affection are closely linked is nearly double that of the men. . . . While women develop physically somewhat earlier than men, large proportions of them take a more intense conscious interest in sex later than the men do. At the same time, it appeared in our interviews that the women had achieved a more mature orientation to sex: that is, they seemed to be more aware of the psychological complexity of sex and to think of members of the other sex more as individuals than as stereotypes (pp. 53, 55).

If women begin to treat sex impersonally, to separate the physical from the emotional and to take on the irresponsible, uncaring attitude more characteristic of men,* I believe we shall be very much the poorer. Barbara Seaman (1972) expresses the fear that "a great many young women are merely swapping the old-fashioned sex-is-for-men sexual masochism of their mothers for a new type of self-punitive behavior. They are trying to copy the *worst* sexual behaviors of men, the promiscuity and exploitation. Sometimes they bed down with people who hardly attract them at all, merely to add another conquest to the 'list' " (pp. 209–10).

The complexity of the issue is illustrated by a comment from a student who read an early draft of this book. In reacting to my statement that for women the circumstances of sexual encounter, assurances of love or affection, mutual trust and desire are often more important than purely physical stimulation, she wrote: "This is often true, but it is so much a function of her place in society and things she has been taught about sex and love that it is impossible

* It should be emphasized that when I refer to what is characteristic of men or women I do not mean that all individuals of each sex exhibit the same qualities. Some women are as impersonal and insensitive as any man; some men are as empathetic as any woman. The differences may be due to varying combinations of prenatal hormonal factors and post-natal influences. But as an empirical fact certain characteristics are more often markedly present in one sex or the other.

to distinguish the natural from the learned! Please mention that this is not necessarily—and not even probably—a 'natural physiological fact' but a product of circumstances. Learning this kind of thing in respected books about our bodies is one way of keeping us from really discovering what we are and freeing ourselves from stereotypes. Similarly, women without children or husbands often feel empty, deprived and lacking—but this is because we have been taught to define ourselves this way. With increasing awareness of this oppression, and more positive feelings about ourselves and our careers independent of subordination to 'our man's' life, these feelings of guilt about not having children, etc., are slowly disappearing. Do you see how this applies in the sexual realm? So there should be some indication more explicitly that this description is not 'truth' or 'woman's nature,' but that it may change as our roles change, and it is not abnormal for a woman to be sexually aroused and active outside of a loving relationship. We are not sick if we can have sexual satisfaction with mere stimulation, without love and security attached, as so many men do."

I agree with this student's assertion of a woman's right to independence and freedom from guilt about sexuality. But I detect in her statement this implication: that women happen to be more empathetic and sensitive than men is merely something that has been forced upon them by society. Given the freedom they are just as capable of being aggressive and impersonal, just as capable of separating the emotional from the physical, just as capable of isolating sex from human relationships as any man. The writer concludes by saying that she doesn't intend to endorse such attitudes by men or women; but she seems to me to protest too much. If such behavior is less than fully humane, should she not rejoice in the fact that most women do not, apparently, respond as readily as men to impersonal sex, rather than protesting their capacity to approximate the less desirable male qualities?

The view that there is a characteristic female attitude to sexuality that is not merely learned is held by many women who are better qualified to assess the evidence than some of the more vocal feminist radicals. Judith Bardwick in her study of "bio-cultural conflicts" (1971) concludes that "there are fundamental psychological differences between the sexes that are, at least in part, related to the differences in their bodies. . . . Predispositions to respond and to perceive similar stimuli may be significantly different between the sexes because of genetically determined differences that have their roots in physiology. The endocrine data and the infant animal and human studies lead to the assumption of general behavioral tendencies that are sex linked and that may be related to the presence or absence of testosterone at a critical stage in development" (pp. 6, 95).

The British ethologist Corinne Hutt (1972) argues at length and with impressive evidence for the biological bases of psychological sex differences. "It is now quite clear," she writes, "that during a critical period in development the secretion of the male gonad organizes first the reproductive tract and structures and then the brain according to a male pattern" (p. 41). "This is not to say that experiences and social influences are unimportant, but these act upon an organism that is *already biased in a male or female direction*" (p. 74). "The male is physically stronger but less resilient, he is more independent, adventurous and aggressive, he is more ambitious and competitive, he has greater spatial, numerical and mechanical ability, he is more likely to construe the world in terms of objects, ideas and theories. The female at the outset possesses those sensory capacities which facilitate interpersonal communion; physically and psychologically she matures more rapidly, her verbal skills are precocious and proficient, she is more nurturant, affiliative, more consistent, and is likely to construe the world in personal, moral and aesthetic terms" (p. 132).

The sociologist Alice Rossi maintains (and cites Anaïs Nin to the same effect) that women have made a mistake in arguing that all sex differences are culturally conditioned. And while she deplores the domestication of women and the mistaken assumption that they should devote all their energies to their children she is equally critical of radical feminists who repudiate marriage: "They haven't experienced the positive side of parenthood so they don't know how to talk about it. They haven't experienced the pleasure of *giving* in marriage, not just *getting* in heretosexual or homosexual relationships. What they have experienced are the consequences of being intelligent, sensitive, idealistic young women in this society. In order to survive they have had to develop thick skins. . . . But the price they pay is high—hesitation to encounter the dependency of a very intimate relationship" (Bermant, 1972, p. 74). The solution, she concludes, is *not* for women to become as competitive, strident and exploitative as men: "Operating under the assumption that men retain, more than women, some evolutionary hangovers in the direction of aggressiveness or male bonding or what have you, means that achieving the highest feminist goals will require more resocialization of men than of women" (p. 75).

What is wanted is not a downgrading of feminine sexuality but an upgrading of the masculine. Women are learning that they are as sexual as men, and that they have no need to apologize for the fact. Rather, they must assert their right to be sexual in their own way and educate men to recognize the joy of sex that is fully personal and responsive. If there are inborn differences these can contribute to the mutual fullness of sexual encounter and union rather than to destructive conflict. Insofar as learned gender roles have distorted human sexuality in our culture men need to modify their behavior at least as much as women.

Margaret Mead (1949) puts the whole issue in proper perspective. She states her persuasion that "women will see the world in different ways than men—and by so doing help the human race see itself more completely" (p. 22). Rather than arguing about whether a woman can be just like a man or vice versa, we should surely be concerned to ask what standards and principles of sexual behavior will be most beneficial—and then seek to encourage and retain these. Complementarity rather than identity, mutuality rather than duplication, openness to growth rather than preservation of the past, freedom to be different rather than an anxious desire to emulate, respect for each sex in its uniqueness rather than enforced similarity—these are surely the desirable consequences of the new female sexual liberation. *Human* sexuality will gain the most if women and men develop their capacities for caring and love without any compulsion to conform to a stereotype—whether it be the stereotype of dependency and subordination or that of aggression and domination.

CHAPTER IX

The Future of Marriage

It is not uncommon for students to daydream about the delights of sexual freedom in the carefree islands of the South Pacific. The idyllic image of life in Polynesia or Melanesia fuses all the attractive elements of these cultures with the advantages of American civilization to form an unrealistic fantasy. The myth includes the individual attention enjoyed by children in our relatively small families, the mixed puberty rites of the *bukumatula,* the uninhibited love affairs of Samoan adolescents, the availability of automobiles and drive-in movies and the intensity of personal relationships we associate with "being in love." But such a culture is a mirage. No single society actually incorporates more than a few of these phenomena. "No human society condones promiscuous or indiscriminate mating. Every culture contains regulations that direct and restrict the individual's selection of a sexual partner or partners" (Ford and Beach, 1951, p. 114). Societies permitting uninhibited sexual activity before marriage usually lack the bare elements of comfort which we take for granted, allow virtually no privacy to their members, develop little depth of personal relationship, enjoy scant opportunity for education or travel and achieve minimal professional or technical skills. In some societies the penalties for premarital sexual intercourse are vicious and rigidly enforced, and others are much more strict than ours in their treatment of those who transgress the social codes governing formal courtship and marriage (Ford and Beach, 1951). Even if it were possible it is doubtful whether any contemporary Westerner (particularly any woman) would actually prefer to grow up in Melanesia. While Margaret Mead's famous Samoans are charming and attractive people we would find the non-sexual aspects of their society, with its strict hierarchy and ritual punctilio, at least as repressive as our own. As Haughton (1971) points out: "Contrary to the western myth, the Samoans were as unromantic as any people could be. Their pleasure in sex was as simple, open and superficial as a child's pleasure in licking an ice-cream cone" (p. 70). The *bukumatula* of the Trobriand Islands seems less attractive if we remember that the brief opportunity for sexual experimentation is followed by an early marriage involving sexual exclusiveness, strict prohibition of adultery and very strong social barriers to divorce (Malinowski, 1927). The Marquesans devote a great deal of their time and energy to developing sexual expertise, and share many partners; but they apparently lack the capacity for strong attachments or deep relationships and have no word to express love (Menard, 1972), though Suggs reports that jealousy is widespread and sometimes violent (Suggs, 1971). Courtship among the Mangaians has to be carried out under a cover of public secrecy, and it is affirmed that "the husband and wife come together only to copulate" (Marshall, 1971).

In any case, we cannot regress to a preliterate way of life, undoing centuries of cultural and technological development, even if we wanted to. We can better direct our energies to considering ways in which our traditional pattern of sexual and marital relationships might be modified as a result of our knowledge of other cultures, in order to establish a more wholesome and mature society.

There are those who claim that a comparison between various cultures demonstrates a cause-effect relation between sexual restraint and social progress. The work of the British social anthropologist, J. D. Unwin, is the most thorough exposition of this view, and it is frequently claimed as evidence that any relaxation of the traditional ideal of premarital virginity and strictly monogamous marriage will lead to the disintegration of our whole social system and the loss of the values of Western civilization. Unwin (1935), after extensive studies of the sexual and social patterns of preliterate communities and ancient civilizations, came to this conclusion:

> By virtue of their inherent nature human beings possess certain potential attributes which enable them, when organized in societies, to display social energy. But this energy cannot be displayed except under certain conditions. If these conditions are not satisfied, there can be no energy; but, if they are satisfied, energy will be displayed, its amount varying according to the degree of satisfaction. The conditions are those of compulsory continence. If the continence is great the energy will be great; if the continence is small, the energy will be small (p. 30).

Effective continence involves, in Unwin's view, "absolute monogamy," which in each civilization in turn has been compromised by the emancipation of married women or an "outburst of homosexuality" (p. 35), and has led to the eventual disintegration of the society.

Unwin's thesis continues to have its proponents, though few anthropologists or historians of culture believe that it is persuasive (Bullough, 1972). Vance Packard (1968) gave the argument a qualified endorsement, and Arnold Toynbee (1964) expressed concern lest early sexual experience undermine Western civilization. A similar view has been advanced recently by Gilder (1973), who sees in feminism, gay liberation and *Playboy* a conspiracy to destroy the institution of marriage, which alone can give continuity and order to human society. The National Alliance for Family Life, which is dedicated to the reversal of the trend towards "permissiveness," has used Unwin's material in its publications. And the sociologist Pitirim A. Sorokin (1964) warned in prophetic terms of the imminent disintegration of our culture:

The sex drive is now declared to be the most vital mainspring of human behavior. In the name of science, its fullest satisfaction is urged as a necessary condition of man's health and happiness. Sex inhibitions are viewed as the main source of frustrations, mental and physical illness and criminality. Sexual chastity is ridiculed as a prudish superstition. . . . Sexual profligacy and prowess are proudly glamorized. *Homo sapiens* is replaced by *homo sexualis* packed with genital, anal, oral, and cutaneous libidos. . . . Our trend toward sex anarchy has not yet produced catastrophic consequences. Nevertheless, the first syndromes of grave disease have already appeared (pp. 151–53).

However, as David Mace (1974), himself an admirer of Unwin's research work, points out: "The weakness of both Unwin's and Sorokin's positions is that they never really examined sexual behavior in any detail. They simply drew a line broadly between sex in marriage as controlled, and sex outside marriage as uncontrolled. As long as a legal marriage represented the acknowledged and exclusive way in which the sexual function could be exercised in accordance with responsible cultural goals, that was a valid choice. But we are now in the process of changing our ideas about the context in which responsible and creative sexual behavior can take place." For example, if the increase of premarital intercourse since 1920 represented merely the extension of the impersonal, irresponsible sex (often with prostitutes) that characterized premarital behavior in the nineteenth century, the possibility might well arise that the fundamental quality of life would be undermined. But if (as seems to be the case) premarital sex is frequently as serious, personal and responsible as marital sex the situation is far less critical and significant.

Unwin did not in fact arrive at his thesis as a result of studying human societies. He was first impressed by Freud's view of the relation between sex and civilization, and then set out to see whether it could be substantiated—though it should be noted that he originally hoped to disprove Freud's theory that civilization has been built up by restraining the gratification of innate desires. Freud believed that the inhibition (as distinct from repression) of sexual desire was absolutely essential to the survival of civilization. "So perhaps we must make up our minds to the idea that altogether it is not possible for the claims of the sexual instinct to be reconciled with the demands of culture. . . . This very incapacity in the sexual instinct to yield full satisfaction as soon as it submits to the first demands of culture becomes the source, however, of the grandest cultural achievements, which are brought to birth by ever greater sublimation of the components of the sexual instinct. For what motive would induce man to put his sexual energy to other uses if by any disposal of it he could obtain fully satisfying pleasure? He would never let go of this pleasure and would make no further progress" (Freud, 1912, pp. 215–16).

Thus, for Freud, the uninhibited satisfaction of sexual desire in adulthood was something to be feared. It was possible only in the realm of fantasy (for the relatively healthy person) or in socially unacceptable behavior or perversion (for the neurotic). "Civilized society is perpetually threatened with disintegration. The interest of work in common would not hold it together; instinctual passions are stronger than reasonable interest. Civilization has to use its utmost efforts in order to set limits to man's aggressive instincts. . . . Hence, therefore, the use of methods intended to incite people into identification and aim-inhibited relationships of love, hence the restriction upon sexual life, and hence too the ideal's commandment to love one's neighbor as oneself" (Freud, 1929, p. 59).

Herbert Marcuse, in *Eros and Civilization* (1955), has effectively challenged the assumption that Freud's position involves the endorsement of the pattern of abstinence and strict monogamy incorporated in contemporary Western culture. He agrees with Freud that the reality principle (represented by the demands of society) has to exercise some control over the instincts for "every form of the reality principle must be embodied in a system of societal institutions and relations, laws and values which transmit and enforce the required 'modification' of the instincts" (p. 46). But he believes that capitalist society has brought about a "surplus-repression" of sexuality in the service of the "performance principle" which allows a particular group to dominate and sustain itself in a privileged position of power and wealth (pp. 44–45). Our culture, in order to keep the masses in subjection, puts an unnecessarily rigid taboo on bodily pleasure and limits acceptable sexuality to genital activity linked with procreation. Any enjoyment of sex as an end in itself is seen (rightly, from the point of view of the establishment) as a threat to order and authority, a diversion from the work ethic which demands man's energies in the service of production and aggression.

Religion contributes to the oppression by its sex-denying ideals enforced by feelings of guilt, and by offering future happiness in return for sexual restraint in this world.

Marcuse therefore calls for a "gradual decontrolling of the instinctual development" (p. 114), the replacement of genital-reproductive sexuality by a "polymorphous sexuality" in which the whole human body becomes an instrument of pleasure rather than a tool of labor, an explosive change leading to a "non-repressive development of the libido under the conditions of mature civilization" (p. 118). He argues that Freud's own position leads not to the acceptance of social controls as we now know them but to a realization of sexual fantasy in "an 'erotic reality' where the life instincts would come to rest in fulfillment without repression" (p. 123) and "the 'lower depth' of instinctual gratification assumes a new dignity" (p. 132). In the new order the organization of labor will be modified to allow satisfaction of basic human needs, both social and sexual, freedom from guilt and fear, the end of repressive restraints, the enjoyment of sensuousness, play and song.*

As a matter of fact significant changes in the sexual structure of our society are already taking place. Whether they will be extended by radical political change or gradually incorporated into the social framework remains to be seen. I think the most important thing is for us to be aware of these changes, to accept them where they contribute to human growth, and to reject them where they threaten the good of the individual and the community. Above all we must seek to cultivate what Marcuse calls the "rationality

* Contrary to frequent misrepresentation, Marcuse does *not* envision a condition of unrestrained instinctual satisfaction which would, he says, lead to a non-society of sex maniacs. He believes that previously taboo areas of human experience will be eroticized and the self-sublimation of sexuality will put an end to concern with goal-oriented, genital-centered sex (pp. 164, 166).

of gratification," so that a new, non-repressive order can develop in which "the sex instincts can, by virtue of their own dynamic and under changed existential and societal conditions, generate lasting erotic relations among mature individuals" (p. 162).

The most significant change lies in the simple fact that marriage no longer plays the traditional role in our society. Now that effective methods of birth control have made possible the enjoyment of sexual relationships at a profound level without the legal commitment of marriage the institution is ceasing to determine the pattern of life. Whereas a decade ago it was pretty much taken for granted that a couple would marry if their relationship became serious, there is now no sense of obligation to give public or permanent expression to the fact. "Singlehood" is a practicable and respectable way of life. There is no overwhelming social pressure to marry unless a couple want to have or adopt a child, and many people, including public figures, live together unmarried for years without embarrassment.*

When people do marry they are no longer necessarily committing themselves for life. Although religious vows are still taken "until death do us part," the average length of a marriage today is just over seven years, and there is one divorce for every four marriages (Olson, 1972). The reasons are many. One is the availability of simpler and less costly procedures for divorce. Another is the decline in the influence of religious prohibitions. A third is the fact that people have higher standards for marriage and are no longer prepared to spend their lives together without personal fulfillment or sexual satisfaction. A fourth is the fact

---

* *The New York Times* (October 14, 1973) reported that between 1960 and 1970 the number of unmarried couples reported in the official census as living together increased by 820 percent—to a total of nearly 150,000.

that in a mobile society the nuclear family has to depend much more on its inner resources, which often prove inadequate. In a family isolated from community in a suburb, or temporarily located by business or professional obligations, an increasing demand is placed on the marital partners to be companion, lover, friend and therapist to each other. Fulfilling the role of housewife or breadwinner is no longer sufficient. "As American society has become increasingly mechanized and depersonalized, the family remains as one of the few social groups where what sociologists call the primary relationship has still managed to survive. As such, a greater and greater demand has been placed upon the modern family and especially the modern marriage to provide for affection and companionship. Indeed, it is highly plausible to explain the increased rate of divorce during the last 70 years, not in terms of a breakdown in marriage relationships, but instead, as resulting from the increased load which marriage has been asked to carry" (Balswick and Peek, 1971).

Some have mounted a frontal attack on the whole institution of marriage. One student wrote in a term paper: "I think my generation has a pretty cynical attitude. . . . At the same time that our parents were telling us about love and honor and responsibility, we saw our own parents as well as the other families around us fighting, hating, hurting each other. No kid with two eyes or two ears could possibly avoid knowing how many adults were fooling around, living together for the children's sake, deceiving each other, living in despair" (LeShan, 1971, pp. 7–8). Kate Millett (1970) calls marriage "civil death," "domestic slavery," an oppressive instrument of male supremacy and a tool of the state frustrating revolutionary change. "The sexual revolution," she writes, "concentrated on the superstructure of patriarchal policy, changing its legal forms, its more flagrant abuses, altering its formal educational patterns, but leaving the socialization processes of temperament and role differentiation intact" (pp. 176–77). Germaine Greer (1971), while acknowledging that if marriage is a chosen way of life and not a necessary condition of existence it can be an experience of a creative kind, is hardly less damnatory. Like Millett, she quotes Engels to the effect that "the modern individual family is founded on the open or concealed slavery of the wife" (p. 217), and concludes that "if women are to effect a significant amelioration in their condition it seems obvious that they must refuse to marry" (p. 317). Laws (1971) reviewed the vast field of literature on "marital adjustment" and came to the conclusion that it was dedicated to conditioning women to accept a subordinate and personally restrictive role.

Some radical feminists assert that lesbianism represents not only a viable alternative to marriage but a superior type of relationship. Barbara Seaman (1972) quotes this example:

There are four advantages to lesbianism. First, a woman understands another woman's body so much better than a man can. Other women are better lovers. Second, women have prettier bodies, soft curves and smooth skin instead of bones and balls and hair in scratchy inappropriate places. Women are more cuddly and nicer to love. Third, women can't knock each other up. You don't have to spoil the beauty of the act messing around with birth control. You don't get frantic when your period is late. Fourth and most important, in a healthy lesbian relationship, you are equals as men and women in our society cannot yet be (p. 68).

Kelly (1972) has stated flatly that "a woman would be foolish to be entirely open and trusting with a member of the class whose very status is founded on her debasement. . . .

Because of the inequities between men and women in this culture, because equality is necessary to the full growth of the ability to love, and because of the essential equalness of women, the most perfect development of the ability to love, where women are concerned, can occur only in a homosexual context. . . . Because men occupy a superior social position and are schooled to covet power over others in order to maintain that position, they can rarely accept others, especially women, as equals."

The various experiments with different types of commune and multilateral or group marriage reflect a widespread desire to find an alternative to traditional marriage bonds (Ramey, 1972). Personally I welcome any form of association with promise of more creative human relationships. I see no reason why a society as pluralistic as ours in other respects should not allow for and welcome a variety of types of marriage, and it seems ridiculous that a single pattern is (at least in theory) imposed throughout our society. It is significant that a report presented to the United Presbyterian Church in 1970 included this statement: "The church has at least the obligation to explore the possibilities of both celibate and non-celibate communal living arrangements as ethically acceptable and personally fulfilling alternatives for unmarried persons" (*Sexuality and the Human Community,* p. 36).

Some communes are unrealistically utopian, some provide a refuge for people who are too immature to establish deep relationships and some are obsessed with drugs or under the sway of demagogic leaders who destroy rather than enhance personal growth (LeShan, 1971; Ald, 1971). Some, such as the Twin Oaks Community (Kinkade, 1973), represent serious and hopeful attempts to provide a context for personal and sexual growth. But communes seem to provide only temporary satisfaction for most people.

Many of their members pair off and establish a dyadic relationship which is often eventually formalized in marriage —probably with a greater prospect of being successful than if the couple had not the opportunity of getting to know each other in depth in the setting of the commune. A not unsympathetic observer comments: "A prominent personal historical characteristic common among tribal family members is a childhood emotional isolation associated with a wistful seeking to gain love and security in a new kinship system. They try to reconstitute the loving, accepting, undemanding family unit which was either lost or never existed at all. The tribal family members act out a Camelot-like legend, seeking a brotherhood and sisterhood of sharing, loving, and growing. Sadly, they often frustrate their own yearnings through naiveté, inexperience, or lack of discipline" (Downing, 1970).

Group marriages, usually involving two or three couples, often depend for their success on the existence of earlier strong dyadic partnerships (Constantine and Constantine, 1971). Most of them do not provide a permanent alternative for the participants, and after a year or two lead to new combinations of couples in traditional marital units (Kilgo, 1972; Constantine and Constantine, 1972). The experience may help to establish more mature personal relationships which provide a better basis for a second marriage or for the renewal of the original bond. In other words, group marriage is often not so much a repudiation of marriage as a criticism of its form and a possible means to its improvement.

Continued evolution rather than revolution seems likely to be the operative principle in the future of marriage (Olson, 1972). The family, which originated in some form between two million and a hundred thousand years ago, which exists in all known human societies (Gough, 1971) and which is probably an integral part of any specifically human community (Mair, 1971), is not about to disappear from the scene. While more of today's students will remain single the majority will eventually marry. The rate of marriage was higher in 1970 than it had been at any time since 1950, and only 3 or 4 percent of the population remains unmarried throughout life.

Despite the funereal orations proclaimed over the institution and the justifiable attacks on its actual and potential oppressiveness, more than three out of four men *and women* rate their marriages as "very happy" or "happy" (Renne, 1970). This is admittedly a highly subjective criterion. But what to others may appear to be (and might be for them) a very unsatisfactory marriage can be, for the couple involved, at least preferable to any alternative. Cuber and Harroff (1966) have identified five types of marriage ranging from "conflict-habituated" to "total" or "intrinsic," but they point out that "persons in all five are currently adjusted and most say that they are content, if not happy. . . . the five types represent *different kinds of adjustment* and *different conceptions of marriage*. This is an important concept which must be emphasized if one is to understand the personal meanings which these people attach to the conditions of their marital experience" (p. 61).

Even those whose marriages end in sadness often look back on the experience as valuable (and more often than not divorced people remarry). Abigail McCarthy, the wife of the former senator and presidential candidate, concludes her moving autobiography by writing (after her husband had terminated the relationship):

I do not regret that for thirty years, in the words of Simone de Beauvoir, "I spontaneously preferred another existence to my own." I think I am a much richer person for having shared that existence and because of the sharing that my own existence developed dimensions otherwise outside its scope. Nor do I see any sense in putting it all behind me as if it had not been because, quite obviously, it is part of me (p. 435).

There are at least two reasons for the persistence of marriage. In the first place, nobody has yet produced a more satisfactory medium for the nurture and education of children. Harlow's famous studies of rhesus monkeys suggest that there is no adequate substitute for the personal interaction of mother and child (Harlow and Harlow, 1965). "I have a deep ambivalence about communal child-rearing, or group marriage," says Alice Rossi. "From what one reads, they seem transient, unstable, often superficial, at least in their American manifestations. From studies of children reared in the kibbutzim, communal child-rearing seems to succeed in reducing any marked pathology, but at the expense of unique creativity. I do not myself see any meaningful substitute for the intimacy and sense of rootedness that a good marriage or a good parent-child relationship gives to one's life" (Bermant, 1972).

It is surely when a couple undertakes to raise a family that society has a proper concern about the quality and permanence of their union. And the decision to have or adopt children is a significant milestone in the growth of love. It represents a high degree of confidence in one's capacity to live harmoniously and creatively with another person, as well as mutual interests and ideals and more than superficial sexual attraction. This seems to be the appropriate point at which to give love a public and a binding commitment. Marriage can best serve as the expression of a considered intention (or at least a readiness) to share the time and energy involved in parenthood. It is the announcement of the fruition of a relationship, of two people's readiness in mutual love to give themselves and their future at least for this length of time. It is a request for the assistance of the community and in a religious context of God in the fulfillment of new obligations. The couple say, in effect: "Not only are we emotionally tied to each other, but the evidence of our good faith is that we want the world to share in the knowledge of our life together, and to hold us responsible within our common social existence for the vows we make to each other," and for our obligations as parents" (Hough, 1969). Perhaps what we need is a return to the assumption that marriage is a long-term commitment (to discourage irresponsible parenthood) and much freer acceptance of premarital sexual activity (to encourage responsible mate selection).*

A second reason for the persistence of marriage is that whatever its problems, marriage does represent a unique opportunity for the development of interpersonal relationships. Snow (1971) has argued persuasively that it may prove to be the only effective bastion against the encroachments of a technological, impersonal way of life. The psychiatrist Anthony Storr (1963) states that "a happy marriage perhaps represents the ideal of human relationship—a setting in which each partner, while acknowledging the need of the other, feels free to be what he or she by nature is: a relationship in which instinct as well as intellect can find expression; in which giving and taking are equal; in which each accepts the other, and I confronts Thou" (p. 126). A discussion among a group of marriage counselors entitled

* Or possibly a two-tier arrangement such as that proposed by Mead (1966) or Packard (1968). In both cases a period of marital adjustment would normally be followed by a permanent commitment. But if the initial experience of living together proved unhappy that relationship could be terminated relatively easily. Parenthood would either be delayed until the second stage (Mead) or would automatically initiate it (Packard).

"Save the spouses, rather than the marriage," which reflected deep awareness of the pitfalls of marriage, concluded with this reflection: "The one-to-one commitment is hard as hell, but no viable alternative presents itself that is as rewarding, as intimate and as significant. . . . we persist in this monumentally imperfect one-to-one equation because when it is bent to our purpose, as it can be; when the neuroses have been meshed and the impossible expectations compromised, it satisfies more of the human needs —for comfort, for continuity, for nurture, for the central connection—than it fails to satisfy, and more than any other equation we know" (*New York Times Magazine,* August 13, 1972). The best-selling book *Open Marriage* (O'Neill and O'Neill, 1972) while advocating major changes in marriage, is essentially a defense of it along these lines: "The one-to-one relationship, whether it is realized through monogamy or within other forms of marriage, fulfills man's profoundly human needs—those developmental and psychological needs for intimacy, trust, affection, affiliation and the validation of experience. It need not be permanent, exclusive or dependent, but the relationship of two people to each other allows a closeness and psychological intimacy that no other kind of relationship offers" (p. 24).

Marriage of the future, while preserving the central concept of a union between two people, will be different from its past. "Open marriage" will allow much more opportunity for personal development and separate interests, putting an end to the assumption that one partner has to subordinate his or (more commonly) her individuality to the other. Associations with members of the other sex will not be regarded as necessarily destructive of the "primary relationship" of husband and wife (O'Neill and O'Neill, 1972). While the ideal of a lifelong commitment will probably persist, a couple will be free to terminate a marriage that has ceased to be satisfying or beneficial to themselves and their children.

Cuber and Harroff (1966) found that among the "significant Americans" only a small proportion enjoyed marriages that were truly fulfilling. But they also found that perhaps a third of their subjects acknowledged that their problems sprang in part from poor mate choices. The fact that today's generation will only get married when they have a better basis to assess their mutual qualities, and that family planning will reduce some of the more serious strains on the husband-wife relationships, gives reason to hope that marriage has a brighter future (Winch, 1970). Hopefully an increasing proportion of couples will enjoy this experience described by Cuber and Harroff: "To feel deeply content with a mate—to feel deep, moving involvement with his physical and psychological presence—is a kind of well-being which they find richly rewarding and sustaining. From this fountainhead flow positive influences for physical and mental health, as well as for creativity. A substantial professional literature in psychiatry confirms the testimony of those in the Intrinsic Marriages that the vitality of their kind of relationship radiates far beyond the elemental ecstasy of the pairing" (p. 141).

Appendix

The purpose of this appendix is to provide some basic facts about birth control, abortion and venereal disease relevant to the needs of college students. I have had the inestimable advantage of the criticism and suggestions of Philip M. Sarrel, M.D., Director of the Sex Counseling Program of the Yale University Health Service, who has checked my facts and saved me from several errors. He is not, of course, responsible for any remaining inaccuracies or for my personal opinions expressed in this appendix or the main part of the book. For fuller information reference should be made to one of the larger textbooks. McCary's *Human Sexuality* (Van Nostrand, Revised Edition 1973) or Katchadourian and Lunde's *Fundamentals of Human Sexuality* (Holt, Rinehart and Winston, 1972) are thorough and reliable. *Our Bodies, Our Selves* (Simon and Schuster, 1973), the *Birth Control Handbook* and the *VD Handbook* (available for twenty-five cents each from P.O. Box 1000, Station G, Montreal 130, Quebec, Canada) are excellent sources by and for women that should also be read by men. *The Pill* by Robert W. Kistner, M.D. (Delacorte, 1969) is a thorough discussion intended for the layman.

BIRTH CONTROL

Why do people still conceive when they don't intend to? Many students are remarkably ignorant about the process of reproduction and the available methods of birth control, though few will admit it. Some have a totally irrational belief that "it won't happen to me." Those who intend to avoid intercourse but succumb to pressure or passion are likely to be unprotected "on principle." Many are careless in the use of contraceptives that are available to them. With adequate information and facilities pregnancy rates can be reduced to less than 1 percent of the female student population, but at many schools 6–15 percent of the women conceive unnecessarily.

Carelessness or forgetfulness leading to unintended pregnancy may be due to unconscious motives. The method used or proposed may be aesthetically distasteful, and the temptation to take a chance that much more serious. Many women still associate the idea of premeditated protection with wantonness or promiscuity and, being unable to accept the fact of their own sexuality, fail to assume the responsibilities that go with it. They prefer to be able to justify intercourse as the result of overwhelming passion or male pressure, and to this end avoid taking rational precautions in advance. Some have an unacknowledged desire to bear a child as a demonstration of their femininity.* Some do so in order to punish themselves for what they internally feel to be a transgression of their moral values: by enduring (or risking) the consequences of pregnancy they come to terms with guilt about the act of intercourse.

Some students disregard the need for birth control out of a mistaken desire to express their personal independence against parental prohibitions. Men often assume quite wrongly that any girl who agrees to heavy petting or intercourse has automatically equipped herself for casual sexual

---

* It is now thought that the man's desire to demonstrate masculinity by fathering a child may also sometimes be a hidden factor in the failure to use a contraceptive.

activity. Many fail to check that their partner is protected, and some couldn't care less whether she is or not. Some men and women assume that because abortion is available as a last resort there's no reason to worry about pregnancy, ignoring the fact that abortion is *never* just a matter of a simple visit to a doctor's office. If there is one minimal obligation involved in any relationship of trust and care between two people it is: Don't lay the burden of unwanted conception on your partner.

Can you become pregnant without intercourse? Yes, though it is very rare. It is not necessary for the penis to be inserted in the vagina for conception to take place. If the male ejaculates near the vulva, sperm may make their way into the vagina, even if the female is a virgin. Petting, particularly if fingers are inserted in the vagina, may add to the risk. Any couple who are sleeping together without actually having intercourse should therefore take precautions against conception. A tampon inserted in the vagina provides good protection. The chances of pregnancy are not high, but the risk is not worth taking.

Can you become pregnant without having an orgasm? Absolutely. The male's orgasm is usually (but not always) necessary to start the sperm on their way to the fallopian tubes. The female's orgasm plays no known part in the process of reproduction. Some women hold back from sexual release on the mistaken assumption that this will prevent conception—the result may be that they establish a pattern of sexual inhibition and/or that they find themselves with an unwanted pregnancy.

Are you always safe during a period? No. While the

probability of pregnancy is not great, it is possible to conceive as a result of intercourse while menstruating. A woman who has a short cycle (twenty to twenty-five days) will ovulate between the sixth and eleventh day after the beginning of her period. If the period lasts four or five days, and if intercourse takes place towards its end, sperm may be present and fertile when the ovum is released, and conception will occur. Women who have even occasionally short menstrual cycles should therefore take precautions during their period. Those on the pill are protected at this time. Those using an IUD should check before and after intercourse to ensure that the device is still in place. A diaphragm *can* be used during menstruation, as well as foams or a condom.

What parental permission is necessary to obtain contraceptives? In virtually every state some contraceptives—condoms, vaginal foams, spermicidal creams and jellies—can be purchased at pharmacies and drug stores without difficulty or expense. In the great majority of states any woman eighteen years of age or over can seek and receive contraceptive care without parental permission. Even in states where there is a legal restriction many doctors or clinics will provide contraceptive advice and services to a student. No case is known in which a physician has been taken to court and charged with an offense in providing help for birth control.

There has been a dramatic rise in the number of college health services offering full gynecological and contraceptive services in the past ten years. *Any student needing help who is unable to obtain it on campus or locally should contact a branch of Planned Parenthood, or call or write: Family Planning Information Service, 300 Park Avenue South, New York, N.Y. 10010 (telephone 212: 677–3040).*

What happens if you go to a doctor for a contraceptive?
Many women are anxious about their first gynecological
examination, and some fear that the doctor will take the
opportunity to deliver a moral lecture on sexual behavior.
On the whole, however, these fears are ill-founded, particularly if the physician is accustomed to student needs
and attitudes. Most doctors are sensitive to the initial embarrassment felt by women in exposing the genitals for
examination. Here is an account by a Yale student reprinted (with permission) from *The Student Guide to Sex
on Campus*:

After I told the gynecologist my name and address and some
sort of medical history, I asked him how I could get birth control pills because I wanted to sleep with my boyfriend whom I
love very much. The gynecologist asked me a few questions
about my sexual experiences up to that time, and then he told
me that he would be able to write me a prescription for birth
control pills. We talked a little about how the pills worked
(mostly he told me), and then he showed me into the examination room. I had my period at the time, and I really thought (I
really hoped) that for that reason the doctor would not want
to examine me then. But he did, and I was kind of glad to get
it over with—not because of any unpleasantness, just because
of the apprehensions about it. It was really a relief—the examination took only about two minutes, in which time the
doctor was able to check my breasts, vagina, cervix, uterus, and
ovaries. He even pushed my uterus a little so I could feel it by
putting my hand on my abdomen! There was no pain at all,
and it really was very comforting to know that all was right
inside of me. I saw the doctor a month or two later for a
checkup to see if and how the birth control pills were affecting me. Again, all was OK, and I left for the second time with
confidence that, even though I would not be going to this particular gynecologist for the rest of my life, pelvic examinations
and gynecologists in general were not to be feared.

Which methods of birth control are most effective?
Failures in birth control are not simply due to the mechanical imperfection of a particular method. They also arise because some contraceptives are unsuitable for certain people, some are more likely to be forgotten or incorrectly used and some (like the rhythm method) require an unreasonable degree of measured restraint for most students. Taking these factors into account the following five methods are recommended. Except for the pill, which all authorities regard as the most reliable, it is impossible to list them in any absolute order of effectiveness. Any method used regularly is more effective than one used irregularly. Individual circumstances may make a contraceptive that is theoretically effective quite ineffective. The diaphragm properly fitted and in place is very reliable; a condom carelessly applied can be useless.

Further details about the use and effects of each type are given in succeeding answers. It is very important to know how to employ the method you choose, and highly advisable to have professional advice as to which is the most appropriate.

The Pill is in fact a group of oral contraceptives containing various combinations of synthetic compounds (similar in effect to estrogen and progesterone). It requires a doctor's prescription, and at least a week's usage in the first cycle before the woman is protected. By far the most reliable method when taken regularly, but contraindicated for women with certain health problems. Cost: $20–$25 for a year's supply plus doctor's fee for check-ups (twice a year).

A Diaphragm is a rubber cup inserted in the vagina so as to cover the neck of the womb (the cervix). Initially it must be fitted by a doctor, and then reinserted by the woman before intercourse. Very effective when properly applied and used in conjunction with a spermicidal cream or jelly. Cost: $5 plus doctor's or clinic's fee.

An Intrauterine Device (IUD) is a small plastic or metal shape inserted by a doctor in the uterus and left in place for two or more years. This is probably the most effective method after the pill for women who have borne a child, but those who have not done so sometimes have difficulty in retaining an IUD. Cost: $25–$100 including the doctor's fee—much less in a clinic.

Vaginal Foams (not to be confused with foaming *tablets* which are less effective) are chemical spermicides inserted into the vagina with a plastic applicator from an aerosol can before each act of intercourse. They can be purchased without a prescription from drug stores or pharmacies. Cost: about fifteen cents per application.

A Condom ("rubber" or "French letter") is a very thin sheath (usually made of synthetic rubber) that the male slips over the penis before intercourse. They should be purchased from drug stores or pharmaceutical companies and *not* from a vending machine. Cost: from twenty to fifty cents each.

Which methods of birth control are least effective? Creams and jellies without a diaphragm, foaming *tablets*, suppositories and sponges smeared with spermicide are all much better than nothing, but significantly less reliable than the methods listed above.

The rhythm method is very unreliable unless the woman has very regular periods and both partners are capable of organizing their sexual activity according to a strict schedule based on a daily chart of the woman's body temperature on waking each morning. Enforced abstinence for fifteen days or more in each menstrual cycle imposes severe strains on people of student age. Except for those few Roman Catholics who still regard the official teaching of their church on this subject as binding, rhythm cannot be commended as a viable method of birth control. Those who feel bound to use it should do so only under the direction of a doctor or a family planning adviser.

Withdrawal, or *coitus interruptus,* is extremely risky. It requires that the male withdraw his penis completely from the female's genitals just before ejaculation. If he does not, sperm may be deposited in or near the vagina and cause pregnancy. In any case sperm may be discharged during intromission some time before ejaculation occurs, and are quite capable of penetrating to the fallopian tubes and causing pregnancy. Some psychiatrists believe the practice of withdrawal has harmful emotional effects on both partners.

Douching, or washing out the vagina after intercourse, is as like to force sperm into the uterus as to prevent them from entering. The use of a bottle of Coke as a post-coital douche, as suggested by Reuben in *Everything you always wanted to know about sex,* is a highly dangerous practice which may result in serious infection, permanent sterility or even death from embolism.

"Feminine hygiene" products such as Norforms are not only worthless as contraceptives but if used improperly may harm the tissue of the vagina. It should be (but unfortunately is not) unnecessary to tell students that hot baths (for men), urinating after intercourse (for women), or having intercourse standing up (for both) are not contraceptive methods.

How safe is the pill?   As a contraceptive the pill is virtually 100 percent effective when taken regularly, which usually means daily for twenty or twenty-one days in each menstrual cycle. The instructions given with the brand prescribed by the doctor must be carefully observed. Omitting to take the pill on one day is not likely to result in pregnancy, but a couple of days' forgetfulness can make conception possible. In such cases intercourse should be avoided until after the next menstruation or another contraceptive (such as a condom or vaginal foam) used in addition.

The pill is a potent medication which produces profound hormonal and metabolic effects. It prevents pregnancy by inhibiting ovulation, by thickening the mucus of the cervix so that sperm do not enter the uterus and by disrupting the cyclic growth of the lining of the uterus so that it is not receptive to the fertilized ovum if conception does occur. One type of pill (sequential) contains only synthetic estrogen for the first part of the series and a combination of synthetic estrogen and progesterone for the second part. *Oracon* is a brand prescribed by many doctors for those women for whom sequential pills are suitable. The other (combination) type, which contains both (synthetic) estrogen and progesterone throughout the cycle is more reliable for most women. The brands generally recommended are: *Demulen 1, Norlestrin 1, Norinyl 1, Ortho-Novum 1/50* and *Ovral.*

A third type of pill, often called the minipill, contains only progesterone. While it eliminates the problems caused by the use of estrogen for some women, it has proven significantly less reliable in preventing pregnancy and produces severe irregularities in the menstrual cycle of many users.

Health problems connected with the use of the pill fall

into three categories: (1) A number of women experience minor, temporary inconveniences such as occasional nausea, fluid retention, breast enlargement, slight bleeding between periods, depression or minor vaginal infections. These often disappear without treatment, but if they persist or become serious they can usually be relieved with medication. (2) As with all powerful drugs (even aspirin or penicillin) there is a slight risk of serious complications for any user. But it is generally agreed that the benefits outweigh the risks for the great majority of women: pregnancy and childbirth are much more dangerous. Provided that she has an annual gynecological check-up, including a breast examination and a pap test, a normally healthy woman need have no fear of cancer resulting from the use of the pill. Earlier fears that it was linked to cancer of the breast or cervix have now been discounted by further research. (3) For a few women the pill represents an unacceptable risk. Those who have or have had a stroke, blood clots, heart defects, serious migraine headaches, endocrine disorders or cancer should not use the pill. Certain other health problems such as high blood pressure, diabetes, kidney disease, hepatitis or psychiatric illness require careful medical supervision.

In brief: *any woman should have competent medical advice and regular check-ups, but in the absence of specific contraindications the pill can be used with confidence.* Indeed, for some it brings the added side-benefits of lighter periods and freedom from pain or depression associated with menstruation. Soon after the use of the pill is discontinued normal ovulation is restored, fertility is not affected and there are no ill effects on babies born subsequently.

How does a diaphragm work?   A diaphragm is made of

soft rubber with a spring rim that fits over the cervix and prevents sperm entering the uterus. Each woman must be individually fitted by a doctor who chooses the appropriate size and type and shows her how to insert and remove the device (using a plastic or metal inserter if desired). A diaphragm can be fitted on a woman who has not had intercourse, but it should be checked again by the doctor after her first intercourse. Every woman should have periodic check-ups to ensure that the size and techniques of insertion are still correct.

When properly used and smeared with spermicidal cream or jelly on both surfaces and on the rim, a diaphragm is a very effective (though not infallible) contraceptive.

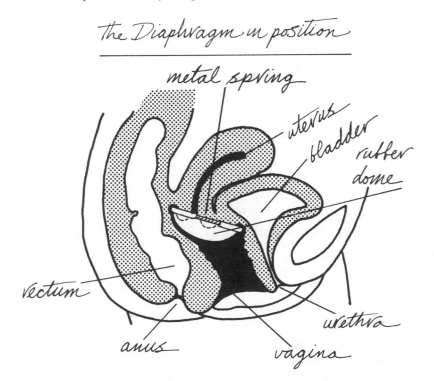

The Diaphragm in position

metal spring

uterus

bladder

rubber dome

rectum

anus

urethra

vagina

When correctly positioned it cannot be felt by either partner during intercourse. Additional spermicidal cream, jelly or foam must be inserted in the vagina with an applicator before a second act of intercourse takes place.

The disadvantage of the diaphragm over the pill or the IUD is that it must be inserted and removed for each coital sequence—not *more* than two hours before and not *less* than six hours after. It must then be washed, dried and powdered with corn starch and occasionally checked for cracks and holes.

The following creams and jellies are among the most reliable for use with a diaphragm:

> *Certane Vaginal Creme*
> Vogarrell Products Co., Los Angeles, Ca.
>
> *Contra Creme*
> Research Supplies, Pine Station, Albany, N.Y.
>
> *Lorophyn Jelly*
> Eaton Laboratories, Norwich, N.Y.
>
> *Creemoz Vaginal Creme*
> Larre Laboratories, Inc., Yonkers, N.Y.
>
> *Lactikol Vaginal Jelly*
> Durex Products, Inc., New York, N.Y.
>
> *Ortho-Gynol Vaginal Jelly*
> Ortho Pharmaceutical Corp., Raritan, N.J.
>
> *Koromex Jelly*
> Holland-Rantos Co., Inc., New York, N.Y.

How reliable is an IUD for a woman who has not been pregnant?   The IUD, like the pill, has the great advantage of eliminating any need for contraceptive procedures at the time of each act of intercourse, and is thus far less likely to fail because of forgetfulness or inadequate application. Once inserted by a doctor (usually during the menstrual period) the IUD is very effective in preventing pregnancy —probably by rendering the uterus unreceptive in some way to a fertilized ovum.

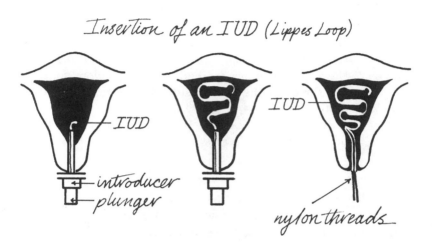

Insertion of an IUD (Lippes Loop)

Although most IUDs have nylon threads attached by which they can be removed (by a doctor) they are usually not felt by either partner during coitus. Side effects are usually temporary: they may include pain following insertion, irregular bleeding, heavy menstrual flows for a few cycles, some interference with hormonal balance and occasional vaginal infections. But serious complications are very uncommon with the latest IUDs, *no cases of cancer resulting from their use have been documented* and the woman's later capacity for child-bearing is in no way impaired.

One limitation of the IUD is that some women spontaneously expel the device (usually in the first three months). Since expulsion usually occurs with the menstrual flow it can go unnoticed (particularly if the woman experiences cramps at menstruation), and unwanted pregnancy can result. This problem is more common among women who have never been pregnant, but IUDs are now being developed specifically for these women.

Students using an IUD should observe the following procedures:

1. Have the device selected and fitted by a gynecologist or in a clinic specializing in birth control procedures.
2. Use a supplementary method (foam or condom) for the first three months and at midcycle (the time of ovulation).
3. Check the presence of the IUD once a week by feeling the threads at the cervix.

What vaginal foams are recommended?   Opinions as to the effectiveness of spermicidal vaginal foams as a contraceptive vary greatly, but many authorities believe that when correctly used they are more reliable than a diaphragm or condom, and they may be the preferred method for those who cannot use the pill or an IUD. If used with a condom they afford almost complete protection. There are seldom any side effects other than minor allergic reactions, and the chemicals do not interfere with sexual sensation. However, they have one disadvantage that often results in their ineffective employment: *a vaginal foam to be an adequate safeguard should be inserted not more than an hour before intercourse.*

Vaginal foams (to be distinguished from foaming *tablets*, which are less effective) are sold, without a prescription, in aerosol cans with a plastic applicator. *Delfen* (Ortho Pharmaceutical Corp., Raritan, N.J.) and *Emko* (Emko Co., St. Louis, Mo.) are the most widely recommended. After shaking the container the applicator must be filled with the foam, inserted into the vagina as far as it will go, and *then withdrawn half an inch so that its end is close to the cervix.* The plunger must then be fully pushed in and held in that position while the applicator is removed. The procedure should be repeated for any subsequent acts of intercourse, or if the woman gets up from the bed before intercourse. Douching should be avoided for six to eight hours after intercourse, but the woman can use the toilet or take a shower.

Application of a Vaginal Foam

uterus

cervix

applicator

vagina

How reliable is a condom?   When properly used a condom is as effective as any method except the pill, it has no side effects, it is easily accessible and it provides some protection against venereal disease. If used with a vaginal foam a condom affords almost complete protection. The chances of a condom breaking in use are one in three hundred if it has been properly stored and applied. On the other hand some find that it interrupts the spontaneity of sex or dulls the male's sensation—though the latter objection is less common with modern condoms and may be overcome by using the more expensive skin type.

Condoms purchased from drug stores or pharmaceutical companies or family planning agencies are subject to FDA manufacturing tests and can be relied on: those purchased from vending machines should be avoided. Condoms should be kept in the container in which they are packaged, *not* in a wallet or pocket, and it is not advisable to reuse them.

For effective protection the following procedures are important:

1. Unroll the condom over the penis before *any* penetration of the vagina takes place, taking care to avoid tearing the rubber.
2. Leave a half-inch at the end of the condom (or the "teat" if it is of this type) extending beyond the penis (to contain the semen at ejaculation), and squeeze this space while unrolling the condom so that the air is not trapped there.
3. Pull back the foreskin, if not circumcised, before applying the condom.
4. Lubricate the outside of the condom after it is on the penis with some contraceptive foam, cream or jelly (unless it comes prelubricated), but *not* with vaseline or petroleum jelly.
5. Withdraw before there is significant loss of erection holding the upper end of the condom tight against the base of the penis to avoid spilling semen and sperm in or near the vaginal opening.

The penis must not be inserted in the vagina after the condom has been removed unless the man has urinated and

washed his penis with soap and water. Attempting to re-
place the condom with a clean one without these precautions may easily lead to impregnation. The following brand
names are thoroughly reliable:

Shadow-Enz, Youngs Drug Corp., New York, N.Y.

Sheik, Julius Schmid, Inc., New York, N.Y.

Trojan-Enz, Youngs Drug Corp., New York, N.Y.

Ramses, Julius Schmid, Inc., New York, N.Y.

Guardian (lubricated), Youngs Drug Corp., New York,
N.Y.

Naturalamb (rolled, lubricated), Youngs Drug Corp.,
New York, N.Y.

XXXX (Fourex) (non-slip, skin, premoistened), Julius
Schmid, Inc., New York, N.Y.

Is there a "morning after" pill?   Yes. Several estrogen
compounds taken within three days after intercourse are
very effective in preventing pregnancy. They can only
be obtained by prescription through a doctor or a college
health service. While their use in emergency situations
such as rape, unprotected intercourse or the failure of a
birth control device may be advisable, interception (as
it is technically called) should not be used as a regular
contraceptive technique or relied on as an alternative to
other methods.

Any doctor will need information about the circumstances under which intercourse took place before agree-
ing to prescribe these strong drugs. He will give a pelvic
examination to check the presence of sperm and to establish whether the woman is pre- or post-ovulatory. He will
not prescribe interception for someone with a history of

migraine, hepatitis, blood clots, heart disease or drug addiction.

Some types of these pills (including DES, or diethylstilbestrol) are now thought to carry a very slight risk of cancer in a female child of the user when taken during pregnancy. Alternatives such as ethinyl estradiol or Premarin are now preferred. If there are no contraindications these are a safe and reliable solution to a critical situation. Where there is a danger of complications it may be wiser to have a menstrual extraction if the risk of unwanted pregnancy is high (see p. 210).

What happened to the "male pill"?   Several lines of research are still being pursued in the hope of finding a reliable and acceptable means of controlling the production of sperm or of rendering sperm incapable of fertilization. So far, however, these have not been successful. Serious side effects, including breast enlargement, the loss of sex-drive, permanent infertility and the danger of prostatic cancer, appear to be associated with the administration of hormones to men. One project came to an abrupt conclusion when it was found that the compound made it impossible for the user to drink alcohol even in small quantities. Another sperm-inhibiting androgen is prohibitively expensive to manufacture. Recent research, using a combination of progestogen and testosterone, seems to offer hope of a usable male contraceptive pill in the reasonably near future.

What new contraceptives for women are on the horizon? Experiments are being made with progesterone injections or implantations which would provide protection for several months or even years at a time; but the danger of permanent sterility is involved and until this problem is resolved the method is unacceptable to most women. A more promising method of administering progesterone is a silastic ring which the woman inserts in the vagina at the beginning of each period. This technique, which is still being tested, has only minor side effects and does not interfere with normal menstruation since the ring is removed after twenty-one days.

A new and more effective type of IUD, the "copper T" or "copper 7," which releases copper (an anti-fertility agent) into the uterus is currently undergoing evaluation.

Is vasectomy or sterilization a feasible procedure for a student? Yes, for those who have no intention of ever having a child. Vasectomy is a simple surgical procedure that can be performed in a doctor's office and involves the severance and tying of the ducts carrying sperm from the testicles to the penis. It does not affect the male hormones or normal sexual response, including ejaculation, and after about six weeks makes conception virtually impossible. The major disadvantage is that the possibility of reversing the operation is not high—70 to 80 percent of such attempts fail to result in fertility. Sperm banks are not available to most people, and their long-term reliability is unknown. Experiments with reversible vasectomy through the insertion of tiny valves in the male ducts point to an interesting possibility for the future but offer no immediate solution.

Female sterilization can now be carried out with a laparoscope in an operation lasting only about thirty minutes. A form of reversible sterilization is being developed, but in the great majority of cases sterilization makes it impossible for the woman ever to bear a child.

Although vasectomy or sterilization is legally permitted in some states for any man or woman age eighteen or over, it is unlikely that a college student (other than in exceptional circumstances) would find a doctor or clinic prepared to perform the operation on anyone under twenty-one.

ABORTION

What are the objections to abortion?   Catholic religious teaching generally holds that from the time of conception the fetus possesses a soul and is essentially a human person: therefore any intentional termination of its life constitutes murder. Some Catholic authorities believe that the soul is not present until the time that the blastocyst is embedded in the wall of the womb (about eight days after conception): the advantage of this position is that it makes it possible for a Catholic to use contraceptive methods which may make the wall of the womb unreceptive and result in the destruction of the blastocyst.

Many people who do not hold any such dogmatic position have serious doubts about abortion. They emphasize the difficulty of establishing any clear point between conception and birth at which the fetus becomes a person with full rights, so that late abortions may in fact involve the destruction of a human being. Furthermore, once the principle of terminating innocent life, even if it is incapable of independent existence, has been accepted, what is to prevent similar arguments being used to justify the killing of mental patients, the terminally sick or the elderly at the convenience of society?

These considerations cannot be dismissed lightly, and abortion cannot be treated by the responsible student as a simple matter of individual convenience. It does constitute the destruction of a unit of life with the potentiality to become a human person. Even if we conclude, as I do, that the act is proper in certain circumstances, it should not be treated lightly. And anyone who has moral objections to abortion should obviously find alternative means of dealing with an unwanted conception. They are discussed below.

It has been argued that the emotional consequences of undergoing abortion are so serious that it is undesirable. Abortion, even under modern clinical conditions, is still a sad, depressing and usually lonely experience for a woman. But except for the woman* with deep religious or ethical objections the effects of an unhappy forced marriage or the strain of bringing up an illegitimate baby are likely to be more serious in the long run. A woman who has other emotional problems may find that these are brought to a head by the experience of abortion; but the same is likely to be true if she marries a man she does not love, looks after a baby she does not want or bears a child and puts it out to adoption. Any brief discussion of this matter is bound to be inadequate. For those facing the issue of abortion I strongly recommend a paperback by Dr. David R. Mace, *Abortion: The Agonizing Decision* (Abingdon, 1972). He presents the different points of view with clarity and non-judgmental fairness.

What are the alternatives to abortion?   Marriage is the solution to unwanted pregnancy that our society generally expects and urges. The pressure should be resisted at all costs. A couple who have been planning marriage and whose educational goals and career prospects are not disas-

---

* The woman has, quite rightly, the primary responsibility for a decision about abortion. But the father of the child is very often involved emotionally. Most unwanted pregnancies are not the result of one-night stands (for those occasions proper precautions are usually taken) but of carelessness during an extensive relationship. The argument that the woman has the right to determine the outcome of a pregnancy as if the fetus were merely a malignant growth in her womb oversimplifies the situation.

trously upset may be able to overcome the serious strains of a marriage that starts out with the wife pregnant. But some who were quite confident of their love before an unplanned pregnancy discover that this crisis shows up basic suspicions, distrust, unreadiness for permanent commitment or other problems that were unsuspected before. It is noteworthy that in Sweden, where the unmarried mother and illegitimate baby are far less subject to social embarrassment than in this country, a considerable portion of *engaged* couples decide not to marry once pregnancy occurs. This suggests that they find that becoming responsible for the conception of a baby does not cement their relationship but destroys it.

A "shot-gun" marriage has advantages for the families involved (particularly the woman's) because it saves them from the stigma of illegitimacy. It may relieve the guilt felt by the couple involved. But in the long run the consequences are likely to be disadvantageous for all concerned —including the baby. Premarital pregnancy is a frequent precursor of early divorce because the task of adjusting to marriage is greatly complicated by early financial burdens and social restrictions. Husband and wife are liable to blame each other (perhaps silently) for the predicament. Worst of all the unwanted child may become the object of unconscious resentment or jealousy. A baby brought up by people who want a child and cannot have their own is more likely to develop a happy, strong personality than a child who is blamed secretly by its parents for having tied them unwillingly to each other.

The other alternative, of course, is for the woman to have the baby out of wedlock. In this country an unwed mother faces severe problems if she decides to bring up her child by herself. But the task is not impossible, particularly with supportive friends and family, and this is a better alterna-

tive than marriage if there is no serious relationship between the parents. But probably the best resolution, in this
case, is to arrange through a reliable agency for the child to
be adopted at birth by a couple who can give it the attention and care few unmarried mothers alone can offer. Local
church or state adoption agencies can usually make suitable
arrangements. If necessary, non-sectarian information and
advice about adoption facilities and procedures can be obtained from the following:

> Child Welfare League of America
> 67 Irving Place, New York, N.Y. 10003 (telephone 212:
> 254-7410)

> Florence Crittenden Association of America
> 201 North Wells, Room 1216, Chicago, Ill. 60606 (tele-
> phone 312: 726-0673)

What is the legal situation regarding abortion?   In January 1973 the Supreme Court ruled that up to the end of
the third month of pregnancy the decision is entirely one
between the woman and her physician. For the next six
months a state may make regulations to safeguard the
mother's health—such as licensing facilities for abortions.
During the last ten weeks of pregnancy a state may, if it
wishes, proscribe abortion unless it is necessary to preserve
the life or health of the mother.

The existing state laws on abortion at the time of the
ruling were (with the exception of Alaska, Hawaii, New
York and Washington) much more restrictive. It will be
some time before the Supreme Court ruling is effective
throughout the country, but there is little doubt that eventually the Court's position will be enforced, and many doctors have already begun to follow its guidelines. Anyone

wanting an abortion and having difficulty obtaining one legally should consult one of the agencies listed below (page 214). *In no circumstances should any woman submit to an illegal abortion at the hands of a medical quack, or even by a qualified doctor in secretive circumstances.* Such treatment carries a severe risk of infection, hemorrhage, sterility or death.

How early can you know if you are pregnant?   A hormone carried in the bloodstream of a pregnant woman can be detected in her urine ten to fourteen days after she misses a period, so a woman can usually know within a month of conception that she is pregnant. Missing one period is not necessarily evidence of a pregnancy (sheer anxiety about the possibility may be the reason), but a pregnancy test should be done if a period is two weeks late. Increased size or firmness of the breasts, enlargement or darkening of the nipples or "morning sickness" are common early symptoms.

Any woman who has reason to think she may be pregnant should consult a doctor or clinic *at once,* stressing that it is an emergency if she has difficulty getting an appointment. If she is less than two weeks overdue and the chances of unwanted pregnancy are considerable (for example if she has had unprotected intercourse about the time of ovulation), she should discuss with the doctor the possibility of having a menstrual extraction (or menstrual induction). This is a simple procedure with very few complications, sometimes performed in the doctor's office, which terminates any possible pregnancy. While a doctor may prefer to have the result of a pregnancy test he will perform this operation if the woman's emotional condition and personal circumstances make it specially difficult to wait for confirmation of pregnancy.

If a urine test shows no evidence of pregnancy, yet menstruation does not occur within another week or two, a woman should insist on a second test since there are false readings in 5 percent.

How late can you have an abortion? With modern equipment and competent care abortion can be performed up to the twenty-eighth week of pregnancy, but after the twentieth week it involves major surgery, high costs and the possibility that the woman will have to have any future deliveries by Caesarian section. Ideally a woman who is going to have an abortion should do so before the end of the first trimester—that is, within twelve weeks of the first day of her last period.

What methods are used in abortion today? *Up to 12 weeks* the suction method is most commonly used. A sterile "vacuum aspirator" sucks the fetal tissue from the wall of the uterus in a three- to five-minute procedure. The operation is often carried out with only a local anesthetic in an out-patient clinic or in a doctor's office. The woman can usually return to normal activity in a few hours. The cost is between $100 and $200.

Some doctors still prefer to use the older method of dilation and curettage (D & C), which involves scraping the uterine wall gently with a metal loop. A local anesthetic is sometimes used, and only a couple of days' recuperation are usually needed.

From 12–16 weeks abortions are not usually carried out in the United States because of the size of the uterus at this stage. In Britain a combination of vacuum aspirator and D & C is used.

From 16–24 weeks the preferred method is now to inject

a concentrated salt solution (under local anesthetic) into the amniotic sac in which the embryo is suspended, resulting in contractions within a few hours. The subsequent labor is usually brief, but the experience can be emotionally harrowing. The cost is between $300 and $700.

From 24–28 weeks (or earlier if for some reason alternative methods are unsuitable) a hysterotomy is usually performed. This must be distinguished from a hysterectomy which involves the removal of the uterus. In a hysterotomy the fetus is removed through a small incision in the abdomen below the pubic hairline, but although this is major surgery and involves slight risk it does not interfere with the woman's reproductive system. General anesthesia, several days' hospitalization and convalescence are required, and the cost is high: at least $1,000.

A simpler and safer procedure using prostaglandins (a substance found in human tissue) is currently in the experimental stage. The prostaglandins, administered by intravenous injection requiring no anesthetic, cause uterine contractions which expel the embryonic tissue. This method seems to eliminate the occasional complications of other procedures and is highly successful with pregnancies of less than eight weeks' duration.

What are the risks in legal abortion?   Any surgery carries some slight risk, and this rises as the length of the pregnancy and the complications of the abortion increase. But with trained professional care abortion is no more dangerous than a tonsillectomy. A study of more than forty thousand abortions carried out in the United States in 1970 and 1971 found no case of death among more than thirty thousand women aborted during the first trimester, and only four among more than ten thousand in the second trimester

—only one of which was directly and specifically attributable to the abortion procedure. These figures are considerably lower than the number of deaths expected in the same population as a result of carrying a pregnancy to full term.

A competently performed abortion has no permanent aftereffects. Sexual activity can be resumed in two to four weeks.

Is self-induced abortion dangerous? Yes: both terribly dangerous and totally ineffective. Hot baths, strenuous activity, drinking alcohol, taking quinine or purgatives have no effect whatsoever. When a woman does abort after doing any of these things the abortion is not caused by them but would have happened anyway.

Nothing that is swallowed can cause abortion without causing death or severe harm to the mother. Inserting anything solid into one's uterus can easily cause death from infection, hemorrhage or embolism. Forcing liquids such as soap solutions, alcohol, potassium permanganate or lye into the uterus can result in burning of the tissues, shock and death. Pumping or blowing air into the uterus or drawing it out with a vacuum cleaner is almost immediately fatal. Abortion carried out by any person other than a qualified M.D. or a specially trained physician's assistant is also a highly dangerous and (now that the Supreme Court has declared abortion legal) totally unnecessary risk.

How can you get information about abortion facilities? Now that the Supreme Court has ruled against state laws denying the right to abortion, it should be possible to obtain reliable information from any doctor, medical bureau, clinic or health service. Failing this try the nearest Planned Parenthood center. If there is none write or call one of the following (do not respond to advertisements or offers of assistance from commercial referral organizations):

Family Planning Information Service (Planned Parenthood), 300 Park Avenue South, New York, N.Y. 10010 (telephone 212: 677-3040)

Clergy Consultation Service on Abortion, 55 Washington Square South, New York, N.Y. 10012 (telephone 212: 447-0034)

Problem Pregnancy Information Center, Box 9090, Stanford, Ca. 94305 (telephone 415: 329-9000)

Zero Population Growth Referral Service, 726 Miami Pass, Madison, Wis. 53711 (telephone 608: 238-3338)

Abortion Referral Service, 4224 University Way N.E. Seattle, Wash. 98105 (telephone 206: 634-3460)

Local sources of information on abortion are fully listed in *Abortion: A Woman's Guide* published by Abelard-Schuman (1973) for Planned Parenthood of New York City.

VENEREAL DISEASE

What are the chances of getting a venereal disease? More than two million people in the United States now have gonorrhea and more than a hundred thousand have infectious syphilis. Another half a million people will contract gonorrhea in any single year and eighty thousand more will become infected with syphilis. More than half of these are under twenty-five, and the rate is increasing more rapidly in this age group: in some communities 10 to 20 percent of adolescents and young adults have gonorrhea. Venereal diseases are not restricted to the poor or to urban centers, but are prevalent in rural and suburban communities and among professional and upperclass families as well. Many people spread VD without knowing that they are carriers. Homosexuals are an increasing source of infection. Although VD is not automatically caught from an infected person, *any student who has intercourse with another person who may have had intercourse before is at risk,* even though the incidence on campuses is lower than in the general population. Since both gonorrhea and syphilis can be cured quite easily with modern drugs *anyone who has reason to suspect infection should immediately seek medical attention.*

What precautions should one take against VD?   The most effective safeguard, of course, is to avoid intercourse unless you are quite sure your partner has not slept with anyone else. Failing this find out if there is any reason to think he or she is infected or has had intercourse with someone who was. Many so-called "lovers" do not have sufficient concern for their partners to warn them of this risk. If there is suspicion of danger the male should use a condom in addition to any other form of birth control the woman may have. If the situation is only discovered after intercourse, washing the genital areas with soap and water immediately after contact may materially reduce the chances of infection, but a medical examination should be done in any case. Some doctors will give a dose of penicillin or one of the tetracyclines to protect against VD if there has been exposure to infection. Finally, adequate knowledge about the initial symptoms of VD and readiness to seek medical attention immediately if these appear is essential. In this case VD will prove to be a minor inconvenience rather than (as it can be) a major disaster.

Can you get VD without intercourse?   Yes, though the chances are slight. While the dangers of infection from a toilet seat or towel are infinitesimal, intimate sexual contacts other than actual intercourse can spread these diseases. Gonorrhea can be spread by anal or oral-genital contact. Syphilis can be spread through kissing, if the mouth comes into contact with the open sores of an infected person, through oral-genital acts or through anal intercourse.

What are the symptoms and effects of gonorrhea?   Men usually (*but not always*) notice a thin clear mucous discharge from the penis, three to five days after infection, but possibly as early as a day or as late as two weeks after. Within a day or two the discharge becomes thick and creamy, white, yellow or greenish-yellow in color. There is usually pain (sometimes severe) or burning when urinating. The urine is cloudy and may contain a little blood. These symptoms begin to disappear after about two weeks, but the man can still infect others. In some cases a painful abscess forms in the prostate. In others there is pain and swelling in the testicles and groin eventually (if untreated) leading to sterility. Treatment with penicillin or other antibiotics is rapidly effective and eliminates permanent complications.

Women are much less fortunate than men because they are more likely to experience no warning symptoms for some weeks or months after infection, when they may notice an irritating green or yellow-green vaginal discharge, a burning sensation when urinating or an ache in the lower back or abdomen. Many first realize they have gonorrhea when they observe its symptoms in an infected male partner. Unrecognized and untreated infection can spread through the uterus to the fallopian tubes resulting in a condition called salpingitis which can cause severe pain and sterility. While early antibiotic treatment can prevent permanent damage, failure to observe the presence of infection in time may make it impossible for the woman ever to conceive or to bear a child. If a pregnant woman has gonorrhea when her baby is born the infant's eyes may be seriously damaged if treatment is not initiated immediately.

What are the symptoms and effects of syphilis? About three weeks after intercourse with an infected person (though it may be as soon as ten days or as late as three months) a sore or chancre appears on or near the genitals, the anus or the mouth. The chancre is a dull red bump about the size of a pea when it first appears, though it may not be visible in women when it occurs on the cervix or vaginal wall. It soon develops into an open sore but it is painless and does not bleed easily. In men there may be some swelling of the lymph glands in the groin. If left untreated the chancre heals within one to five weeks and the infected person may think he or she is healed; however the disease continues to develop and the person is still infectious.

If untreated the secondary phase occurs about six weeks (though as early as two weeks and as late as six months) after the first symptoms appeared. This consists of a generalized skin rash which does not hurt or itch, usually consisting of raised rubbery hard bumps on the chest, back, arms, legs, face, palms and soles. It is often accompanied by painless swelling of the lymph glands in the armpits and neck, sometimes by malaise, frequent headaches, nausea, constipation, pain in the bones and muscles and low fever. Once again, if not treated, these symptoms disappear spontaneously in two to six weeks and the patient may think the disease has ended. However, while he or she ceases to be contagious after about a year, the syphilis remains latent and in one out of every two untreated cases eventually leads to other complications, possibly including injury to the heart or the brain resulting in paralysis, insanity and/or death. Children born to women who have untreated syphilis while pregnant may die before or soon after birth or suffer from syphilis themselves.

Anyone with a sore on the sexual organs should have an examination immediately, even though most sores are not syphilitic. A thorough physical check and blood tests may be necessary, but syphilis (even when latent) can be effectively cured by a variety of antibiotics.

What happens if you seek treatment for VD?   You will either receive the appropriate treatment and be assured of full recovery or your fears that you have VD will be put to rest (several minor infections have symptoms similar to those of gonorrhea and syphilis). You will be asked to give the names of anyone from whom you may have caught the disease and they will be asked to undergo diagnosis and, if necessary, cure. They will not be told who provided information about them, and in many places strict confidence is assured through the use of code numbers instead of names. Obviously you do not have to give names, but if you do not do so *you must be sure to warn all the people possibly involved so that they can seek treatment.* The only way to reduce the incidence of VD and the consequent suffering is through honest recognition of the facts and sensible, unembarrassed attention to the problem as a medical, not a moral, issue.

Many people fail to take the elementary precaution of seeking treatment for VD out of fear or shame that their parents will come to know about it. But in most states you do not need parental permission for medical treatment of VD, and while the doctor or clinic will probably have to report the fact to the local health authorities it will not usually be communicated to anyone else without your consent. Nor is any cost involved if you go to a clinic or health service.

References

The following list includes only books and articles quoted or referred to in the text. It is not by any means a complete list of works read or used in the writing of this book. Even less is it a full bibliography on the subject of sexuality, which would require a volume of its own. The date given after the author's name is that of first publication. A date in parenthesis following the publisher's name indicates the date of the edition to which reference is made, where this differs from that of the original.

A short list of selected paperbacks for further reading will be found on page 239.

Abramson, Paul	1973	"The Relationship of the Frequency of Masturbation to Several Aspects of Personality and Behavior," *Journal of Sex Research*, May.
Adelson, Edward R. et al.	1973	"How do you advise the Man who is Overly Concerned about Female Orgasm?" *Medical Aspects of Human Sexuality*, March.
Ald, Roy	1970	*The Youth Communes*, Tower.
Alston, Jon P. and Tucker, Francis	1973	"The Myth of Sexual Permissiveness," *Journal of Sex Research*, February.
Altman, Dennis	1971	*Homosexual—Oppression and Liberation*, Avon.
Arafat, Ibtihaj and Yorburg, Betty	1973a	"Drug Use and the Sexual Behavior of College Women," *Journal of Sex Research*, February.
	1973b	"On Living Together without Marriage," *Journal of Sex Research*, May.

Ardrey, Robert   1966   *The Territorial Imperative,* Delta (1968).
Arieti, Silvano   1972   *The Will to Be Human,* Quadrangle.

Bailey, Derrick   1952   *The Mystery of Love and Marriage,*
  Sherwin   Harper.
                      1955   *Homosexuality and the Western Chris-*
                              tian Tradition, Longmans, Green (Lon-
                              don).
                      1959   *Sexual Relation in Christian Thought,*
                              Harper.
Balswick, Jack O.   1971   "The Inexpressive Male: A Tragedy of
  and Peek,   American Society," *The Family Coor-*
  Charles   *dinator,* October.
Bardwick, Judith   1971   *Psychology of Women: A Study of Bio-*
                              Cultural Conflicts, Harper & Row.
Bell, Robert R.   1966   *Premarital Sex in a Changing Society,*
                              Prentice-Hall.
Bell, Robert R.,   1968   *Studies in Marriage and the Family,*
  ed.   Crowell.
Bell, Robert R.   1972   "Sexual Satisfaction among Married
  and Bell, Phyllis   Women," *Medical Aspects of Human*
                              Sexuality, December.
Bell, Robert R.   1970   "Premarital Sexual Experience among
  and Chaskes, Jay   Coeds, 1958 and 1968," *Journal of Mar-*
                              riage and the Family, February.
Bell, Robert R.   1972   *The Social Dimensions of Human Sex-*
  and Gordon,   *uality,* Little, Brown.
  Michael, eds.
Bengis, Ingrid   1972   *Combat in the Erogenous Zone,* Knopf.
Bennis, Warren   1970   "Norman O. Brown's Body," *Psychology*
                              Today, August.
Bermant, Gordon   1972   "Sisterhood is Beautiful," *Psychology*
                              Today, August.
Bernard, Jessie   1968   *The Sex Game,* Prentice-Hall.
Berne, Eric   1964   *Games People Play,* Grove.
Bertocci, Peter A.   1967   *Sex, Love and the Person,* Sheed and
                              Ward.
Bieber, Irving   1962   *Homosexuality,* Vintage (1965).
  and Others

Blaine, Graham B. 1967 "Sex and the Adolescent," *New York State Journal of Medicine,* July 15.

1968 "Sex Among Teenagers," *Medical Aspects of Human Sexuality,* September.

Bonhoeffer, Dietrich 1953 *Letters and Papers from Prison* (enlarged edition), Macmillan (1972).

Borowitz, Eugene 1969 *Choosing a Sex Ethic: A Jewish Inquiry,* Schocken.

Boston Women's Health Book Collective 1973 *Our Bodies, Our Selves,* Simon & Schuster.

Bovet, Theodor 1958 *A Handbook to Marriage,* Doubleday.

Broderick, Carlfred and Bernard, Jessie, eds. 1969 *The Individual, Sex and Society,* Johns Hopkins.

Brown, Norman O. 1959 *Life Against Death,* Random House.

1966 *Love's Body,* Random House.

Bruns, J. Edgar 1967 "Old Testament History and the Development of a Sexual Ethic," *The New Morality* (ed. Dunphy, William), Herder.

Bullough, Vern L. 1972 "Sex in History: A Virgin Field," *Journal of Sex Research,* May.

Burgess, E. W. and Wallin, P. 1953 *Engagement and Marriage,* Lippincott.

Cadwallader, Mervyn 1966 "Marriage as a Wretched Institution," *Love, Sex and Identity* (eds. Gould, James A. and Iorio, John J.), Boyd and Fraser (1972).

Casler, Lawrence 1969 "This Thing Called Love Is Pathological," *Psychology Today,* December.

Cavanagh, John 1969 "Rhythm of Sexual Desire in Women," *Medical Aspects of Human Sexuality,* February.

Christensen, Harold T. 1971 "Scandinavian Vs. American Sex Patterns," *Sexual Behavior,* December.

Christensen, Harold T. and Gregg, Christina 1970 "Changing Sex Norms in America and Scandinavia," *Journal of Marriage and the Family,* November.

Clark, LeMon   1970   "Is There a Difference between a Clitoral and a Vaginal Orgasm?" *Journal of Sex Research*, February.

Clor, Harry M., ed.   1971   *Censorship and Freedom of Expression*, Rand McNally.

Cole, William Graham   1959   *Sex and Love in the Bible*, Association.

Comfort, Alex   1968   *The Anxiety Makers*, Panther (London).

Commission on Obscenity and Pornography   1970   *Report of the Commission on Obscenity and Pornography*, Bantam.

Constantine, Joan M. and   1971   "Sexual Aspects of Multilateral Relations," *Journal of Sex Research*, August.

Constantine, Larry L.   1972   "Dissolution of Marriage in a Nonconventional Context," *The Family Coordinator*, October.

Coons, Frederick   1972   Commentary on "Letter from a Father to His Coed Daughter," *Medical Aspects of Human Sexuality*, December.

Cory, Donald Webster and LeRoy, John P.   1963   *The Homosexual and His Society*, Citadel.

Cotton, Wayne L.   1972   "Role Playing Substitutions among Homosexuals," *Journal of Sex Research*, November.

Crosby, John F.   1973   *Illusion and Disillusion*, Wadsworth.

Cuber, John F. with Harroff, Peggy B.   1966   *Sex and the Significant Americans*, Penguin.

Davis, Keith E.   1971   "Sex on Campus: Is there a revolution?" *Medical Aspects of Human Sexuality*, January.

Dedek, John F.   1971   *Contemporary Sexual Morality*, Sheed and Ward.

Denfeld, Duane   1973   "The Silent Sex Game," *Sexual Behavior*, February.

Downing, Joseph   1970   "The Tribal Family and the Society of Awakening," *The Family in Search of a*

Drabble, Margaret — 1969 — *Future* (ed. Otto, Herbert A.), Appleton-Century-Crofts.

1969 — *The Waterfall*, Knopf.

Driscoll, Richard H. and Devis, Keith E. — 1971 — "Sexual Restraints: A Comparison of Perceived and Self-Reported Reasons for College Students," *Journal of Sex Research*, November.

Driscoll, Richard H., Davis, Keith E. and Lipetz, Milton E. — 1972 — "Parental Interference and Romantic Love: the Romeo and Juliet Effect," *Journal of Personality and Social Psychology*, October.

Duvall, Evelyn M. and Duvall, Sylvanus, eds. — 1961 — *Sex Ways in Fact and Faith*, Association.

Eastman, William — 1972 — "First Intercourse," *Sexual Behavior*, March.

Eddy, Harrison P., ed. — 1966 — *Sex and the College Student*, Atheneum.

Ehrmann, Winston W. — 1959 — *Premarital Dating Behavior*, Holt, Rinehart and Winston.

Ellis, Albert — 1963 — *Sex and the Single Man*, Lyle Stuart.

1969 — "The Use of Sex in Human Life," a dialogue between Albert Ellis and David Mace, *Journal of Sex Research*, February.

Ellis, Havelock — 1933 — *Psychology of Sex*, Pan (London: 1959).

Epstein, Gilda F. and Bronzaft, Arline L. — 1972 — "Female Freshmen View Their Roles as Women," *Journal of Marriage and the Family*, November.

Erikson, Erik H. — 1963 — *Childhood and Society* (second edition), Norton.

Feldman, David — 1968 — *Birth Control in Jewish Law*, New York University.

Feller, Richard, Fox, Elaine and Schwartz, Pepper, eds. — 1970 — *The Student Guide to Sex on Campus*, Signet.

Fisher, Seymour   1973   "Female Orgasm," *Medical Aspects of Human Sexuality*, April.

Ford, Clellan S. and Beach, Frank   1951   *Patterns of Sexual Behavior*, Harper (1970).

Freedman, Mervin B. and Lozoff, Marjorie   1972   ". . . some statistical background," *Sexual Behavior*, November.

Freud, Sigmund   1905   *Three Contributions to the Theory of Sex*, Dutton (1962).

1912   "The Most Prevalent Form of Degradation in Erotic Life," *Collected Papers*, vol. 4 (ed. Riviere, Joan), Basic (1959).

1925   "Some Psychological Consequences of the Anatomical Distinction between the Sexes," *Collected Papers*, vol. 5 (ed. Strachey, James), Basic (1959).

1929   *Civilization and Its Discontents*, Norton (1962).

Fromm, Erich   1956   *The Art of Loving*, Bantam (1963).

Gadpaille, Warren J.   1972   "What Is Acceptable Sexual Behavior?" *Sexual Behavior*, July.

1973a   "Innate Masculine-Feminine Differences," *Medical Aspects of Human Sexuality*, February.

1973b   "What Are the Effects of Premarital Sex on the Marital Relationship?" *Medical Aspects of Human Sexuality*, April.

Gagnon, John H. and Simon, William   1968   "Sexual Deviance in Contemporary America," *The Annals of the American Academy of Political and Social Science*, March.

Ganzfield, Solomon, ed.   1961   *Code of Jewish Law* (trans. Hyman E. Goldbin, revised edition), Hebrew Publishing Co.

Gebhard, Paul H.   1966   "Factors in Marital Orgasm," *The Social Dimensions of Human Sexuality* (eds. Bell, Robert R. and Gordon, Michael), Little, Brown (1972).

Gilder, George   1973   "The Suicide of the Sexes," *Harper's*, July.

Gordon, David Cole   1968   *Self Love*, Penguin (1972).

Gough, Kathleen   1971   "The Origin of the Family," *Journal of Marriage and the Family*, November.

Gould, James A. and Iorrio, John J.   1972   *Love, Sex and Identity*, Boyd and Fraser.

Gould, Robert E.   1971   "Single Girls and Sex," *Sexual Behavior*, October.

Granatir, William   1968   "Female Orgasm," *Medical Aspects of Human Sexuality*, April.

Greenberg, Jerrold S. and Archambault, Francis X.   1973   "Masturbation, Self-Esteem and Other Variables," *Journal of Sex Research*, February.

Greene, Gael   1964   *Sex and the College Girl*, Dell.

Greenwald, Harold   1970   Marriage as a Non-Legal Voluntary Association," *The Family in Search of a Future* (ed. Otto, Herbert A.), Appleton-Century-Crofts.

Greer, Germaine   1971   *The Female Eunuch*, McGraw-Hill.
                        1973   "Seduction is a Four-Letter Word," *Playboy*, January.

Group for the Advancement of Psychiatry   1968   *Normal Adolescence*, Scribner.

Hamblett, Charles and Deverson, Jane   1964   *Generation X*, Tandem (London).

Hamilton, William   1956   *The Christian Man*, Westminster.

Harlow, Harry F.   1965   "Sexual Behavior of the Rhesus Monkey," *Sex and Behavior* (ed. Beach, Frank A.), Wiley.

Harlow, Harry F. and Harlow,   1965   "The Effects of Rearing Conditions on Behavior," *Sex Research: New Develop-*

Margaret K.   *ments* (ed. Money, John), Holt, Rinehart and Winston.

Hartogs, Renatus   1967   *Four Letter Word Games: The Psychol*
with Fantel, Hans   *ogy of Obscenity,* Dell.

Hatterer,   1973   "Myths About Homosexuality," *Medical*
Lawrence J.   *Opinion,* January.

Haughton,   1971   *Love,* Penguin.
Rosemary

Hedblom, Jack H.   1972   "The Female Homosexual: Social and
                            Attitudinal Dimensions," *The Homosex*
                            ual Dialectic (ed. McCaffrey, Joseph A.),
                            Prentice-Hall.

Hefner, Hugh M.   1962–65   *The Playboy Philosophy,* HMH Publishing.

Heron, Alastair,   1963   *Towards a Quaker View of Sex,* Wested.   minster.

Hettlinger,   1966   *Living With Sex: The Student's Di*
Richard F.   *lemma,* Seabury.

                    1969   *"Everything But . . . ,"* Guidance Associates.

                    1971   "Sex, Religion and Censorship," *Censor*
                            ship and Freedom of Expression (ed.
                            Clor, Harry M.), Rand McNally.

                    1972   "Sex and the College Student," *Sexual*
                            Behavior, November.

Hoffman, Martin   1969   "Homosexual," *Psychology Today,* July.

Hooker, Evelyn   1957   "The Adjustment of the Male Overt Homosexual," *The Problem of Homosex*
                            uality in Modern Society (ed. Ruitenbeek, Hendrik M.), Dutton (1963).

                    1961   "Homosexuality—Summary of Studies,"
                            Sex Ways—In Fact and Faith (eds. Duvall, Evelyn M. and Duvall, Sylvanus
                            M.), Association.

                    1965   "Male Homosexuals and Their 'Worlds',"
                            Sexual Inversion (ed. Marmor, Judd),
                            Basic.

Horney, Karen   1926   "The Flight from Womanhood," *Femi*
                            nine Psychology (ed. Kelman, Harold),
                            Norton (1967).

	1927	"Inhibited Femininity," *Feminine Psychology* (ed. Kelman, Harold), Norton (1967).
Hough, Joseph C., Jr.	1969	"Rules and the Ethics of Sex," *The Christian Century*, January 29.
Humphreys, Laud	1970	*Tearoom Trade: Impersonal Sex in Public Places*, Aldine.
	1972	"New Styles in Homosexual Manliness," *The Homosexual Dialectic* (ed. McCaffrey, Joseph A.), Prentice-Hall.
Hutt, Corinne	1972	*Males and Females*, Penguin.
Hyde, H. Montgomery	1970	*The Love That Dared Not Speak Its Name*, Little, Brown.

"J"	1971	*The Sensuous Woman*, Dell.
Jackson, Erwin D. and Potkay, Charles A.	1973	"Precollege Influences on Sexual Experiences of Coeds," *Journal of Sex Research*, May.
Jencks, Christopher	1964	"Sex and the College Girl," *The New Republic*, April 4.
Johnson, Warren	1963	*Human Sex and Sex Education*, Lea and Febiger.
	1968	"Muscular Performance Following Coitus," *Journal of Sex Research*, August.

Kaats, Gilbert R. and Davis, Keith	1970	"The Dynamics of Sexual Behavior of College Students," *Journal of Marriage and the Family*, August.
	1972	"The Social Psychology of Sexual Behavior," *Social Psychology in the Seventies* (ed. Wrightsman, Lawrence S.), Brooks/Cole.
Kanin, Eugene J.	1967	"An Examination of Sexual Aggression as a Response to Sexual Frustration," *Journal of Marriage and the Family*, August.
	1969	"Selected Dyadic Aspects of Male Sex Aggression," *Journal of Sex Research*, February.

| | 1970 | "Sex Aggression by College Men," *Medical Aspects of Human Sexuality*, September. |

Karlen, Arno — 1971 — *Sexuality and Homosexuality*, Norton.

Katchadourian, Herant A. and Lunde, Donald T. — 1972 — *Fundamentals of Human Sexuality*, Holt, Rinehart and Winston.

Katz, Joseph and Associates — 1968 — *No Time For Youth: Growth and Constraint in College Students*, Jossey-Bass.

Keen, Sam and Raser, John — 1970 — "A Conversation with Herbert Marcuse," *Psychology Today*, February.

Kelly, Janis — 1972 — "Sister Love: An Exploration of the Need for Homosexual Experience," *The Family Coordinator*, October.

Keniston, Kenneth — 1965 — *The Uncommitted: Alienated Youth in American Society*, Harcourt, Brace and World.

Kephart, William — 1973 — "Evaluation of Romantic Love," *Medical Aspects of Human Sexuality*, February.

Kilgo, Reese Danley — 1972 — "Can Group Marriage Work?" *Sexual Behavior*, March.

Kinkade, Kathleen — 1973 — *A Walden Two Experiment*, Morrow.

Kinsey, A. C., Pomeroy, W. B. and Martin, C. E. — 1948 — *Sexual Behavior in the Human Male*, Saunders.

Kinsey, A. C., Pomeroy, W. B., Martin, C. E. and Gebhard, P. H. — 1953 — *Sexual Behavior in the Human Female*, Saunders.

Kirkendall, Lester — 1961 — *Premarital Intercourse and Interpersonal Relationships*, Julian.

 — 1974 — "Can Premarital Intercourse Be Healthy?" *Explorations in Healthy Personality* (ed. Frick, Willard B.), Shields.

Kistner, Robert — 1969 — *The Pill*, Delacorte.

Klemensrud, Judy — 1968 — "An Arrangement: Living Together for Convenience, Security, Sex," *The New York Times*, March 4.

Kohlberg, Lawrence   1964   "Development of Moral Character and Moral Ideology," *Review of Child Development Research,* vol. 1 (eds. Hoffman, Martin and Hoffman, Lois Wladis), Russell Sage Foundation.

Kroger, William   1969   "Comprehensive Approach to Ecclesiogenic Neuroses," *Journal of Sex Research,* February.

Kronhausen, Phyllis, and Kronhausen, Eberhard   1960   *Sex Histories of American College Men,* Ballantine.

Laing, R. D.   1967   *The Politics of Experience,* Pantheon.

Laws, Judith Long   1971   "A Feminist Review of the Marital Adjustment Literature: The Rape of the Locke," *Journal of Marriage and the Family,* August.

LeShan, Eda J.   1971   *Mates and Roommates: New Styles in Young Marriages,* Public Affairs Committee.

Levin, Max et al.   1972   "Is There Any Difference between 'Vaginal' and 'Clitoral' Orgasm?" *Sexual Behavior,* March.

Levitt, Eugene E.   1973   "Nymphomania," *Sexual Behavior,* March.

Lief, Harold I. and Guthrie, Michael B.   1972   "What It's Like to Live in a Co-ed Dorm," *Sexual Behavior,* December.

Lindner, Robert   1956   "Homosexuality and the Contemporary Scene," *The Problem of Homosexuality in Modern Society* (ed. Ruitenbeek, Hendrik M.), Dutton (1963).

Liswood, Rebecca and Ellis, Albert   1971   "Is premarital chastity desirable?" *Sexual Behavior,* June.

LoPiccolo, Joseph   1973   "Mothers and Daughters: Perceived and Real Difference in Sexual Values," *Journal of Sex Research,* May.

Lorenz, Konrad   1967   *On Aggression,* Bantam.

Lowen, Alexander   1965   *Love and Orgasm,* Macmillan.

Lower, George   1973   *Feelings of Regret Involved in Premari-tal Intercourse,* privately printed.

Luckey, Eleanore   1969   "A Comparison of Sexual Attitudes and
B. and Nass,   Behavior in an International Sample,"
Gilbert D.   *Journal of Marriage and the Family,*
                               May.

Lyness, Judith L.,   1972   "Living Together: An Alternative to
Lipetz, Milton E.   Marriage," *Journal of Marriage and the*
and Davis, Keith   *Family,* May.

Mace, David R.   1972   *Abortion: The Agonizing Decision,* Ab-
                               ingdon.

                       1974   *Sex and Culture: A Study Guide,* The
                               Sex Information and Education Council
                               of the U.S.

MacInnes, Colin   1963   "Coming of Age in Great Britain," *The
                               Spectator* (London), May 3.

Macklin, Eleanor   1972   "Heterosexual Cohabitation among Un-
                               married College Students," *The Family
                               Coordinator,* October.

Maddock, James   1972   "Morality and Individual Development:
                               A Basis for Value Education," *The Fam-
                               ily Coordinator,* July.

Madison, Peter   1971   "The Campus: Coming of Age at Col-
                               lege," *Psychology Today,* October.

Magee, Brian   1968   *One In Twenty,* Corgi (London).

Maguire, Daniel   1968   "Moral Absolutes and the Magisterium,"
                               Absolutes in Moral Theology? (ed. Cur-
                               ran, Charles E.), Corpus.

Mailer, Norman   1971   *The Prisoner of Sex,* Signet.

Mair, Lucy   1971   *Marriage,* Penguin.

Malinowski,   1927   *Sex and Repression in Savage Society,*
Bronislaw   Routledge (London: 1960).

Marcus, Steven   1966   *The Other Victorians,* Basic.

Marcuse, Herbert   1955   *Eros and Civilization,* Beacon.

                       1969   *An Essay on Liberation,* Beacon.

Marshall, Donald   1971   "Sexual Behavior on Mangaia," *Human
                               Sexual Behavior* (eds. Marshall, Donald
                               S. and Suggs, Robert C.), Basic.

Maslow, Abraham 1962 *Toward a Psychology of Being,* Van Nostrand.

Masters, William H. and Johnson, Virginia E. 1966 *Human Sexual Response,* Little, Brown.

1968 "Playboy Interview: Masters and Johnson," *Masters and Johnson Explained* (Lehrman, N.), Playboy Press (1970).

1970 *Human Sexual Inadequacy,* Little, Brown.

1972 "Contemporary Influences on Sexual Response: The Work Ethic," a paper presented at the second SIECUS Citation Dinner, October 18.

Maxey, Margaret 1972 "Beyond Eve and Mary," *New Theology,* No. 9 (eds. Marty, Martin E. and Peerman, Dean G.), Macmillan.

May, Rollo 1966 *Psychology and the Human Dilemma,* Van Nostrand.

1969 *Love and Will,* Norton.

Mayeroff, Milton 1971 *On Caring,* Harper & Row.

McCaffrey, Joseph A., ed. 1972 *The Homosexual Dialectic,* Prentice-Hall.

McCarthy, Abigail 1972 *Private Faces/Public Places,* Doubleday.

McCary, James Leslie 1973 *Human Sexuality* (second edition), Van Nostrand Reinhold.

Mead, Margaret 1935 *Sex and Temperament in Three Primitive Societies,* Mentor (1950).

1949 *Male and Female,* Morrow (1967).

1966 "Marriage in Two Steps," *The Family in Search of a Future* (ed. Otto, Herbert A.), Appleton-Century-Crofts (1970).

Menard, Wilmon 1972 "Love, Marquesan Style," *Sexual Behavior,* September.

Milas, Suzanne 1967 "Why I Believe in Sex before Marriage," *Redbook,* November.

Millett, Kate 1970 *Sexual Politics,* Doubleday.

Money, John and Ehrhardt, Anke 1972 *Man and Woman: Boy and Girl,* Johns Hopkins.

Montagu, M. F. Ashley, ed.	1968	*Man and Aggression,* Oxford.
Moody, Howard	1965	"Toward a New Definition of Obscenity," *Christianity and Crisis,* January 25.
Morris, Desmond	1967	*The Naked Ape,* McGraw-Hill.
Morris, Naomi M. and Udry, J. Richard	1971	"Periodicity in Sexual Behavior in Women," *Medical Aspects of Human Sexuality,* April.
Oberholtzer, W. Dwight, ed.	1971	*Is Gay Good?* Westminster.
O'Connor, John and Wrightsman, Lawrence S.	1972	"Moral Development and the Development of Motives," *Social Psychology in the Seventies* (ed. Wrightsman, Lawrence S.), Brooks/Cole.
Olson, David H.	1972	"Marriage of the Future: Revolutionary or Evolutionary Change?" *The Family Coordinator,* October.
O'Neil, Robert P. and Donovan, Michael A.	1968	*Sexuality and Moral Responsibility,* Corpus.
O'Neill, Nena and O'Neill, George	1972	*Open Marriage: A New Life Style for Couples,* Evans and Lippincott.
Otto, Herbert A., ed.	1970	*The Family in Search of a Future,* Appleton-Century-Crofts.
Packard, Vance	1968	*The Sexual Wilderness,* McKay.
Piaget, Jean	1932	*The Moral Judgment of the Child,* Free Press (1965).
Piper, Otto	1960	*The Biblical View of Sex and Marriage,* Scribner.
Pomeroy, Wardell	1970	"A Comment on the Report of the Commission on Obscenity and Pornography," *SIECUS Newsletter,* April.
Ramey, James W.	1972	"Emerging Patterns of Innovative Behavior in Marriage," *The Family Coordinator,* October.
Ramsey, Paul	1968	"A Proposal to the New Moralists," *Motive,* April.

Reevy, William   1972   "Petting Experience and Marital Success," *Journal of Sex Research,* February.

Reich, Wilhelm   1927   *The Function of the Orgasm,* Noonday (1961).

                          1936   *The Sexual Revolution,* Noonday (1962).

Reik, Theodor   1957   *Of Love and Lust,* Bantam (1967).

Reiss, Ira L.   1960   *Premarital Sexual Standards in America,* Free Press.

                          1967   *The Social Context of Premarital Sexual Permissiveness,* Holt, Rinehart and Winston.

                          1970   "Premarital Sexual Standards," *Sexuality and Man,* Scribner.

Renne, Karen S.   1970   "Correlates of Dissatisfaction in Marriage," *Journal of Marriage and the Family,* February.

Reuben, David   1969   *Everything you always wanted to know about sex,* McKay.

Rhymes, Douglas   1964   *No New Morality,* Constable (London).

Richardson, Herbert W.   1971   *Nun, Witch, Playmate: The Americanization of Sex,* Harper & Row.

Robertiello, Richard C.   1970   "The 'Clitoral vs. Vaginal Orgasm' Controversy and Some of Its Ramifications," *Journal of Sex Research,* November.

                          1973   "One Psychiatrist's View of Female Homosexuality," *Journal of Sex Research,* February.

Robinson, Ira E., King, Karl and Balswick, Jack O.   1972   "The Premarital Sexual Revolution Among College Females," *The Family Coordinator,* April.

Sayers, Dorothy L.   1943   *The Other Six Deadly Sins,* Methuen (London).

Schaefer, Leah Cahan   1973   *Women and Sex,* Pantheon.

Schur, Edwin M., ed.   1964   *The Family and the Sexual Revolution,* Indiana University.

Schwarz, Gerhart   1973   "Devices to Prevent Masturbation," *Medical Aspects of Human Sexuality,* May.

Seaman, Barbara	1972	*Free and Female,* Coward, McCann and Geoghegan.
Sherfey, Mary Jane	1972	*The Nature and Evolution of Female Sexuality,* Random House.
Singer, Josephine and Singer, Irving	1972	"Types of Female Orgasm," *Journal of Sex Research,* November.
Smigel, Erwin O. and Seiden, Rita	1968	"The Decline and Fall of the Double Standard," *Annals of the American Academy of Political and Social Science,* March.
Smith, David E.	1972	"Sexual Practices in the Hippie Subculture," *Medical Aspects of Human Sexuality,* April.
Snow, John	1971	*On Pilgrimage: Marriage in the '70s,* Seabury.
Sonenschein, David	1972	"The Ethnography of Male Homosexual Relationships," *The Social Dimension of Human Sexuality* (eds. Bell, Robert R. and Gordon, Michael), Little, Brown.
Sorokin, Pitirim	1964	"The American Sex Revolution," *The Family and the Sexual Revolution* (ed. Schur, Edwin M.), Indiana University.
Spanier, Graham	1972	"Romanticism and Marital Adjustment," *Journal of Marriage and the Family,* August.
Stafford-Clark, David	1967	*What Freud Really Said,* Penguin.
Stanley, Elizabeth et al.	1973	"Can Women Enjoy Sex without Orgasm?" *Medical Aspects of Human Sexuality,* January.
Steinem, Gloria	1972	"The Moral Disarmament of Betty Coed," *Esquire,* September.
Stekel, William	1950	*Auto-Eroticism,* Washington Square (1967).
Stoller, Robert J.	1968	*Sex and Gender,* Science House.
Stolper, Pinchas	1967	*The Road to Responsible Jewish Adulthood,* Union of Orthodox Jewish Congregations of America.
Storr, Anthony	1963	*The Integrity of the Personality,* Penguin.

	1964	*Sexual Deviation,* Penguin.
	1968	*Human Aggression,* Atheneum.
Suggs, Robert C.	1971	"Sex and Personality in the Marquesas," *Human Sexual Behavior* (eds. Marshall, Donald S. and Suggs, Robert C.), Basic.
Task Force of the United Presbyterian Church	1970	*Sexuality and the Human Community,* Report of a Task Force of the United Presbyterian Church.
Tax, Meredith	1970	"The Woman and Her Mind: The Story of Everyday Life," *Notes from the Second Year: Women's Liberation* (ed. Koedt, Anne).
Teevan, James T. Jr.	1972	"Reference Groups and Premarital Sexual Behavior," *Journal of Marriage and the Family,* May.
Tiger, Lionel	1969	*Men in Groups,* Random House.
Toynbee, Arnold	1964	"Why I Dislike Western Civilization," *The New York Times Magazine,* May 18.
Tunnadine, Prudence	1967	"Advising the Unmarried," *New Christian* (London), July 27.
Unwin, J. D.	1935	*Sexual Regulations and Cultural Behavior,* privately reprinted by Frank M. Darrow (1969).
Vincent, Clark E.	1973	"Side Effects on the Family from Liberalized Sexual Attitudes," *Medical Aspects of Human Sexuality,* June.
Vreeland, Rebecca S.	1972	"Sex at Harvard," *Sexual Behavior,* February.
Walsh, Joseph L.	1967	"Sex on Campus," *Commonweal,* February 24.
Weinberg, George	1972	*Society and the Healthy Homosexual,* St. Martin's.
West, Donald J.	1968	*Homosexuality,* Penguin.
Willis, Stanley E.	1967a	*Understanding and Counseling the Male Homosexual,* Little, Brown.

	1967b	"Sexual Promiscuity as a Symptom of Personal and Cultural Anxiety," *Medical Aspects of Human Sexuality*, October.
Winch, Robert F.	1970	"Permanence and Change in the History of the American Family and Some Speculations as to Its Future," *Journal of Marriage and the Family*, February.
Winick, Charles and Kinsie, Paul	1971	*The Lively Commerce*, Quadrangle.
Yankelovitch Inc., Daniel	1972	*The Changing Values on Campus*, Washington Square.
Young, William C., Goy, Robert W. and Phoenix, Charles H.	1965	"Hormones and Sexual Behavior," *Sex Research: New Developments* (ed. Money, John), Holt, Rinehart and Winston.

Paperbacks for Further Reading

Sex and Society

Normal Adolescence, Group for the Advancement of Psychiatry (Scribner)
Self-Love, David C. Gordon (Penguin)
Sex and the College Student, Group for the Advancement of Psychiatry (Fawcett World)
The Student Guide to Sex on Campus, Yale Student Committee on Human Sexuality (Signet)
Sex is Never an Emergency, Elaine C. Pierson (Lippincott)

Values on Campus

Honest Sex, Della and Rustum Roy (New American Library)
Choosing a Sex Ethic, Eugene B. Borowitz (Schocken)
Psychology and the Human Dilemma, Rollo May (Van Nostrand)
Toward a Psychology of Being, Abraham H. Maslow (Van Nostrand)
The Mystery of Sexuality, Rosemary Haughton (Paulist-Newman)

Sex Before Marriage

Why Wait Till Marriage? Evelyn M. Duvall (Association)
Sex, Love and the Person, Peter A. Bertocci (Sheed and Ward)
Premarital Sexual Standards in America, Ira L. Reiss (Free Press)
Premarital Sex in a Changing Society, Robert R. Bell (Prentice-Hall)

Recreational Sex

Three Contributions to the Theory of Sex, Sigmund Freud (Dutton)
The Sexual Revolution, Wilhelm Reich (Noonday)

Sex Without Guilt, Albert Ellis (Grove)
The Integrity of the Personality, Anthony Storr (Penguin)

The New Sexuality

Life Against Death, Norman O. Brown (Random House)
Love's Body, Norman O. Brown (Random House)
On Caring, Milton Mayeroff (Harper & Row)
The Sex Book, Martin Golstein, E. J. Haeberle and Will McBride (Seabury)

Love and Commitment

The Art of Loving, Erich Fromm (Bantam)
Love and Will, Rollo May (Dell)
Love, Rosemary Haughton (Penguin)
Open Marriage, O'Neill and O'Neill (Avon)

Gay Can Be Good

The Problem of Homosexuality in Modern Society, Hendrik M. Ruitenbeek, ed. (Dutton)
Homosexuality, Irving Bieber and Others (Random House)
The Homosexual Dialectic, Joseph A. McCaffrey, ed. (Prentice-Hall)
Homosexual, Dennis Altman (Avon)
Lesbian/Woman, Del Martin and Phyllis Lyon (Bantam)

Sexual Liberation

Male and Female, Margaret Mead (Dell)
Masculine/Feminine, Betty Roszak and Theodore Roszak, eds. (Harper & Row)
Psychology of Women, Judith M. Bardwick (Harper & Row)
Free and Female, Barbara Seaman (Fawcett World)
Males and Females, Corinne Hutt (Penguin)
The American Male, Myron Brenton (Fawcett Crest)
Man and Woman: Boy and Girl, John Money and Anke A. Ehrhardt (Johns Hopkins)

The Future of Marriage

Patterns of Sexual Behavior, Clelland S. Ford and Frank A. Beach
    (Harper & Row)
Sex and Temperament in Three Primitive Societies, Margaret Mead
    (Apollo)
Civilization and Its Discontents, Sigmund Freud (Norton)
Eros and Civilization, Herbert Marcuse (Random House)
The Family in Search of a Future, Herbert A. Otto, ed. (Appleton-
    Century-Crofts)

ACKNOWLEDGMENTS

Many people have been very generous with their time and helpfully frank in their comments during the writing of this book. Mary Hettlinger, Judith and Bob Goodhand, Eleanore Luckey, Donald Reed and Robert Bennett read the whole manuscript, some more than once. Mary Calderone, Lester Kirkendall, Lorna and Philip Sarrel, David Mace, Maureen Miller, Henry Messer, Thomas Edwards, Rowland Shepard, Fletcher DuBois, Cynthia Caples, Nancy and George Lower and Mary-Kaye Heisler read different parts of the book at various stages.

More students than I can mention by name, at Kenyon, Edinboro State College (Pennsylvania) and Luther College (Iowa) contributed by reading the text, answering questionnaires or participating in discussion.

I am greatly indebted to the faculty of the Public Affairs Conference Center at Kenyon for the use of their seminar room as a workshop; to Marilyn Lyman and the staff of the Planned Parenthood Center of Syracuse, New York, for technical information; to the staff of the Gordon Keith Chalmers Memorial Library for help with books, references and xerox machines; and to Marcella Haldeman for typing the manuscript most expertly.

The selections from *Love and Will* by Rollo May, were reprinted with permission of W. W. Norton & Company, Inc. © 1969 by W. W. Norton & Company, Inc.

Index